the
Good Sex
guide

the
Good Sex
guide

PAULA HALL
JULIAN SLOWINSKI

BARNES & NOBLE

NEW YORK

This edition published by Barnes & Noble, Inc.,
by arrangement with Elwin Street Limited

2005 Barnes & Noble Books

Copyright © 2005 Elwin Street Limited

Conceived and produced by
Elwin Street Limited
79 St John Street
London EC1M 4NR
www.elwinstreet.com

M 10 9 8 7 6 5 4 3 2 1

ISBN 0-7607-7915-5

Designer: Liz Wiffen
Copyeditor: Toria Leitch
For picture credits, see page 144.

Printed in Singapore

Introduction

Sex has the potential to be a profoundly fulfilling experience. As well as offering physical satisfaction and sensual pleasure, sex can unite couples in a way that nothing else can. For many couples, sex is the most intimate expression of their love for each other. It is the act that makes their relationship unique and special.

But this doesn't mean that if we're *in* love, we will naturally and instinctively know how to *make* love. A mutually fulfilling sex life takes time and effort, and above all, it takes commitment. Commitment to be loving, commitment to be open, and commitment to be adventurous.

This book has been written to help you and your partner enjoy better sex. Not just now, but for the rest of your lives together. It begins with helping you to explore the role that sex plays in your relationship and the importance of maintaining intimacy and romance. Next, we explore the real differences between men and women and we shed light on unhelpful beliefs or myths you might hold. "Getting it Together" (Chapter 4) contains some useful tips for seduction and initiation as well as specific techniques for manual and oral stimulation, while "When Two Become One" (Chapter 5) talks about the ins and outs of penetration as well as offering some suggestions for sexual positions.

If you, like many couples, feel your love life may be getting a bit stale, you need the last few chapters of this book. If your regular routines feel more like a rut then you'll get lots of suggestions for spicing it up and revitalizing the passion that the two of you used to share. The final chapter explores how sex changes during our lifetime and offers practical advice for parents young and old. And if you ever feared that sex had a sell-by date, there is plenty to inspire you to keep sexually active long into later life.

But there is one thing you must remember. No matter how dedicated you both are, and how hard you work at it, you will never enjoy great sex *all* of the time. Our sex lives are influenced by so many factors that are beyond our control. All you can do is commit to loving each other and giving sex your best shot.

We hope that reading this book will give you the incentive and information you need to make sex as good as it possibly can be for both of you.

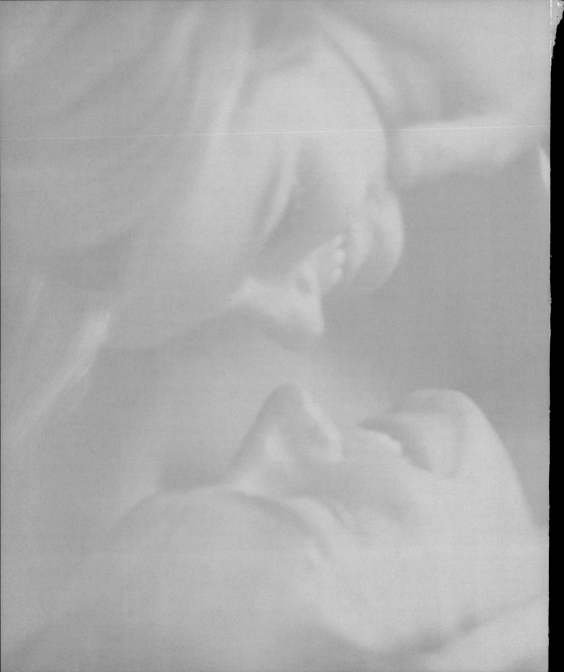

RELATIONSHIP MATTERS

Sex means different things to different people,
and our definition changes over the course of a
relationship and the course of a lifetime. Good sex
happens in good relationships, so how can you build
intimacy, trust, and a passionate sex life?

1

What does sex mean?

If I were to ask you what "sex" meant, what would you say? Would you settle for a physical definition – "intercourse" or "intimate touching"? Or something emotional – "love" or "an expression of affection"? Or perhaps you'd come up with a more holistic definition like "erotic pleasure" or "sensual intimacy"? Then again you might answer by saying what sex symbolizes for you – "the ultimate in physical intimacy" or "a special bond between two people who love each other."

Now, how do you think your partner would answer the same question? Would they say something similar to you? Or something completely different?

Of course, there is no right or wrong answer. Sex means different things to different people and our definition changes over the course of a relationship and the course of a lifetime. Sex is not an inert product that we own or an unchanging personal quality. It is a complex combination of thoughts, emotions, behaviors, and sensations that is intrinsically linked to the relationship we have with our lover.

In the first throes of love we might experience sex as urgent and exciting. An activity that dominates our waking life. As a relationship matures, sex changes. Urgency may be replaced with a more gentle desire and sex may, at times, be loving and romantic, and at other times, playful and passionate. The complexity of humankind with body, heart, and soul, means no two sexual experiences will ever be the same. Whatever your personal definition might be, sex has the potential to be profoundly meaningful. Unfortunately, often it is not.

How important is sex?

Many couples are disappointed with their sex life. Or scared that the good sex they're experiencing now will somehow slip through their fingertips. Increasingly we hear of marriages breaking up because the couple drifted apart, because one of them had an affair, or sometimes because of sexual problems. As the statistics continue to rise, many of us begin to question how good our relationship is. Are we as close as we should be? Is one of us at risk of having an affair? Is our sex life good enough?

In the same way that each of us may have a different definition of sex, each of us may have a different opinion of how important sex is to a happy relationship. Some say it's essential. While for others, it might simply be an optional extra. Again, there is no right answer. It really doesn't matter how important you feel sex is, as long as your partner agrees with you.

Case Story: *Elizabeth and John*

Elizabeth (34) and John (37) had been married for nine years and had two children aged five and three. They went to a counselor because, as John explained, "Things just aren't getting better and I'm sick of waiting." He related how their sex life had diminished to almost nothing since the kids were born.

Elizabeth explained that she had never had as high a sex drive as John, but since the children were born, sex had slipped even further down her list of priorities. The counselor asked how often they would like to have sex. John said he would be happy with two or three times a week and scowled angrily when Elizabeth replied, "Once a month." Before this couple could begin to work together to find a happy medium, it was essential to look at what sex meant to each of them and the role it played in their relationship.

John had come from a very physically affectionate family and he associated sex with love and acceptance. When Elizabeth turned down his advances, he felt deeply rejected. Elizabeth, on the other hand, had been brought up an only child by her mother, after her father left for another woman when she was 12 years old. Although she had always enjoyed sex, she thought John placed too much importance on it. On reflection, Elizabeth wondered if she was saying no to sex as a way of getting back at her father. And John began to appreciate the many other ways that Elizabeth showed her love for him. Over the coming weeks, both began to see sex from a wider perspective and they began to explore ways of increasing both the quantity and quality of their sex life.

Why sex is good for relationships

You can probably think of plenty of reasons why sex is a good idea, apart from sustaining the human race. But you may not be aware of the biochemical role it plays in relationships.

When you have sex your body releases oxytocin, the chemical responsible for human bonding which is also produced by breast-feeding mothers. In fact, whenever you touch, oxytocin is gently released, but when you orgasm, you get a sudden rush. This surge of oxytocin probably accounts for the strong feelings of affection after sex. You can even directly influence the production of this chemical. The more you touch your partner, the more oxytocin you release, and the more oxytocin you release, the more you want to touch. That is how couples bond and can stay bonded.

An active sex life also produces a variety of other chemicals that help us to feel happy and content and more resistant to emotional and physical pain. So when the normal problems of life hit a relationship, the couple that enjoys a regular sex life is more likely to withstand the strains.

Sex is also thought to boost the immune system and increase lean body tissue and thicken skin tissue. One survey concluded that as well as reducing stress levels an active sex life can help make you look four to seven years younger.

Of course, don't forget fun. Someone once said that fun is to intimacy what orgasm is to sex. It's not essential, but it makes it all seem so much more worthwhile.

Committed to good sex

Many people make the mistake of thinking that because sex is natural it should come naturally. But that's not true. The vast majority of us have to work at our sex life, in the same way as we work at our relationship.

That means you both have to make a commitment to talking about your sex life and ensuring that both of you are feeling satisfied. It means that when problems arise (and at some stage in your life, they will), you work through them. It means understanding that sex changes as you age, and that you agree that as this happens, you will make more effort, not less. Couples who still enjoy a great sex life after 10, 20, or even 50 years together, aren't lucky, they are committed.

Building an intimate relationship

Good sex happens in good relationships. If you want to improve your sex life, the most important thing you need to do is improve the quality of your relationship. That means working on intimacy: making sure that both of you feel comfortable and confident with each other.

Most of us would agree that making love has the capacity to make us feel very vulnerable. We are often naked in every sense of the word. So it really shouldn't be surprising that trust is often cited as one of the most crucial elements in a satisfying sexual relationship. Trust that our bodies, our performance, and our desires will be accepted, respected, and cared for.

Improving communication

Expecting your partner to be a mind reader, or thinking that you know what they're trying to say before they've even said it, is a recipe for disaster. At all times you should aim to:

Be a good listener

Listen with your all: Demonstrate you're listening by giving 100 percent of your attention.

Check it out: Make sure you're really hearing what's being said by checking out important details. "So you're saying that . . ."

Empathize: Listen to the feelings as well as the words and let your partner know you've heard everything they have to say.

Be a good speaker

Explain yourself: When you're talking, be ready to give as much information as your partner needs to understand.

Express yourself: As well as giving the facts, make sure that you share your feelings, both good and bad.

---

*"When I really started to hear what my partner was saying, our relationship — including the sexual part — became much better.
I realized that I had been trying to read her mind and,
although listening, I had not been truly hearing her."*

ALAN, 31

Accepting difference

Developing trust also means accepting differences. Because we're all unique, misunderstandings are inevitable. Hopefully most difficulties can be easily resolved, but if issues linger, your sex drive or that of your partner might go down.

If you're heading for an argument, try the following:

Assume the best

Assume that your partner has your best interests at heart and isn't out to get you!

Own your feelings

Don't blame each other for how you feel; accept that ultimately you control your emotions.

Check your circumstances

Be absolutely sure that this argument is necessary. Consider whether you're stressed or tired and might be over-reacting.

Good communication skills take time and effort, and there will always be occasions when both of you fail miserably. When life is getting you down, or stressing you to the limit, little problems can suddenly seem enormous. But if you're confident that both of you are committed to continuing to learn and grow together, you can get through anything.

Quality time

There's an old saying that goes: "Love is best spelt T.I.M.E."
When you spend time with someone, you're saying how
important they are to you. You're saying that other things
can wait; your relationship is the priority.

When couples first fall in love they can't get enough of
each other. They spend every waking moment with each other
if they possibly can. If they're not physically together, they're
on the phone or thinking about each other. Of course this
can't last. But after many years together, some couples go to
the other extreme. They become like ships in the night,
passing each other rarely and with only a hoot of
acknowledgement.

Getting the balance between time together and time apart
is difficult. Living in each other's pockets may leave you with
little to say to each other as every experience has already been
shared. But too much time apart will make you drift apart.
If only there was a tried-and-tested formula – 12 hours a week
together and six hours a week on individual activities. But the
formula is different for every couple. You may also find that one
of you has a greater need for time together or apart than the
other. You need to find out what works best for you as a couple
and compromise where there are differences.

A good sex life is dependent on maintaining a balance
between intimacy and autonomy. It's a lifelong challenge,
but this is the best investment you can make for good sex.

Romance

Romance is essential for keeping couples in touch with each other as loving, sensual human beings. Romance stops you from taking each other for granted and reminds you that you have something special.

Romance isn't just about buying flowers. It includes any kind or fun thing you do for each other or do together. A romantic gesture can be helping your partner to clean the car, remembering to buy a favorite food at the grocery store, sending a text message in the middle of the day to say "you're gorgeous," or snuggling up together and sharing a tub of ice-cream. Romance is any activity that says, "I'm thinking about you."

Keep in touch

Probably the simplest way of building both intimacy and romance in a relationship is to remember to touch each other regularly. That may sound like a really obvious thing to say, but how many times do you and your partner touch?

Often physical touch becomes cursory and perfunctory. A peck on the cheek at bedtime may have as much thought attached to it as putting the cat out. You may not lead a lifestyle that allows you to have long, lingering hugs every few minutes, but you can make a concerted effort to make opportunities to touch. As a bare minimum, touch when you wake up, when you say goodbye, when you return, and when you go to bed. And if you both like relaxing on the sofa in the evening, make sure it's on the same one.

Why not also add to your daily repertoire: a kiss on the back of the neck when your partner's working; a touch on the arm when you ask a question; a caress of the thigh when driving; and a pat on the bottom when you pass on the stairs? Hold hands when you're walking or shopping, lie in each other's arms as you read, watch TV, or talk about your day.

"Every day my partner makes me a cup of tea when I get in from work and massages my feet as I talk about my day. By bedtime I'm always totally relaxed and feeling loved and cherished. Nine times out of 10, we'll have sex if he's in the mood."

SARA, 26

Maintaining a sexual environment

You can't always rely on your partner to turn you on and get you in the mood for sex. Ultimately, you are the one who's responsible for keeping your erotic embers glowing. Once they're glowing, it's a joint responsibility to fan them into a flame of passion, but first you need to tend your embers.

All in the mind

The most important sex organ we have is our brain. If we're not in the right frame of mind for sex, then we're unlikely to want to do it or enjoy it. Good sex starts with a positive sexual attitude. Each of us has a unique view of our sexual selves and of how sex should be. Those views start forming in childhood. Some of us will be fortunate enough to have had lots of positive messages and experiences, while others have to work at seeing sex as a loving and pleasurable encounter.

If you've had negative messages from childhood, or difficult or even traumatic sexual experiences in the past that are impacting your feelings about sex, then please, find someone to talk to about it. An experienced counselor can help you to work through your feelings and to feel more positive about sex.

We're also influenced by the sexual myths that are prevalent in our society. It sometimes seems that as we strive for a more fulfilling sex life, we raise our expectations and create even more anxiety for ourselves. You might find that challenging some common myths will free you to enjoy sex more.

Myth busting

Only young, beautiful people enjoy great sex

Anyone and everyone can enjoy sex if they have a positive sexual attitude. It doesn't matter how old you are, how big you are, how fit you are, or how symmetrical your body is.

Sex should be spontaneous, frequent, and always fantastic

Good sex involves communication and commitment, especially in long-term relationships. Even then, it won't be fantastic every time.

Real sex = intercourse

This is the myth that says if it's not intercourse, it's foreplay. Surely sex is about far more than putting a penis in a vagina. Sex begins when you feel sexy and stops when you don't.

If two people love each other they will know what to do

The human sex drive may be instinctive, but pleasing your partner isn't. Like most things in life, we have to learn and practice.

Sexual liberation means you'll enjoy everything

The sex industry has created a hierarchy, with "beginner's" guides and "advanced" techniques. However, true sexual liberation means accepting that sexual tastes vary and there is no right or wrong or better or worse way to enjoy sex.

Stress: The biggest sexual turn-off

Sex therapy practices around the world are full of people whose sex lives have been wrecked by stress. In an attempt to experience all that life has to offer, many of us try to cram far too much into our lives. Our minds are constantly full of things that need to be done and people who need to be pleased. For some, sex may become just another one of those things.

When we're stressed it's unlikely we'll be interested in sex at all, let alone be able to enjoy it. Stress leaves us feeling physically drained and it distracts us with troubled thoughts.

Learning to manage stress is essential for getting yourself in the right frame of mind for sex. There are lots of excellent stress-management books on the market. If you think you could benefit from learning some new techniques, take some time to check these out. In the meantime, try the following:

❋ *Say no:* Protecting your health and your own relationships is more important than pleasing everyone else.

❋ *Don't be a perfectionist:* Rather than striving for perfection and beating yourself up if everything's not 100 percent, accept that sometimes it's okay for things to be simply good enough.

❋ *Manage your time:* Plan your time carefully and make sure you schedule in times for rest.

❋ *Don't procrastinate:* Stress is often made worse by putting off till tomorrow what you know you should do today. Bite the bullet and do it now; you'll save yourself a load of guilt, worry, and stress.

❋ *Look after your health:* A healthy diet and regular exercise will help you to stay in tip-top physical condition and able to perform at your best and cope with the occasional stressful event.

❋ *Get support:* When you've had a tough day, make sure there's someone you can talk to. It doesn't matter if it's a friend, partner, family member, or colleague from work, just make sure you've got someone who's willing to help you bear the load.

❋ *Be kind to yourself:* This means treating yourself as well as you would your best friend. Remind yourself what a nice person you are and make sure no-one's taking advantage of you – including yourself!

❋ *Laugh:* Laughter really is the best medicine. Laughter not only has a positive impact on your mental health, but research shows it improves your physical health too.

Sexual conditions

Being relaxed is one aspect of being in the right frame of mind. You also need to think about the other physical, emotional, and relationship conditions that you need to enjoy sex.

Those conditions include how we need to feel physically. How is our general health? How tired are we? Have we had too much to drink, or too little? It will also include how we feel emotionally. Are we anxious? Preoccupied or rushed? And finally, our conditions for good sex include how we feel about our relationship. Are we close enough? Is there anger or resentment? Do we feel accepted and valued? If these are things you've never really thought about, have a go at the exercise below:

───────── **TRY THIS NOW!** ─────────

Think back to two occasions when you really, really enjoyed sex.

Now remember two sexual experiences that left you feeling unfulfilled or negative.

Take some time to compare those good and bad sexual experiences. What was different? Consider the physical things that were different, such as the time of day, the location, what you were wearing or the music you were listening to. Think also about the emotional factors. How relaxed were you? What else was going on in your life at that time? Finally, think about how you were feeling about your partner and the relationship.

Use that information to begin to build your personal list of conditions for good sex.

The sensual self

We often pay attention to how our bodies look, but what about how our bodies feel? The skin is the biggest sensory organ that we have and it's often the most overlooked.

Any sex therapist worth their title will encourage their clients to improve their sensual awareness regardless of what brought them into the therapy room. The reason for this is that as your sensual awareness grows, so does your responsiveness. So the more you focus on what you feel, the more you will feel and the more highly tuned you'll be to the diversity of sensation. That means you'll be aroused more easily and also have more control of your arousal.

What's more, it's dead easy to do. Next time you have a bath or shower, make sure you've got a bit of extra time put aside. As the water touches your skin, focus on the sensations. Think about how it feels on different parts of your body. Where is your skin most sensitive? Which areas feel most pleasurable? When you get out of the bath, focus on the sensation of drying yourself. What do you feel when you rub gently, or roughly? How do different parts of your body respond?

Repeating this simple exercise on a regular basis and making an effort to generally become more skin conscious will not only increase your pleasure when you're being touched by your partner, but it will also inspire you to touch them in ways and places you'd never thought of before.

WHAT'S SO SPECIAL ABOUT WOMEN?

No one would question the physical differences
between men and women, but do we really appreciate
the impact those differences make on the way we
think and feel about sex?

2

Women get pregnant

A reckless night of passion can leave a woman carrying a baby for the next nine months, and caring for it for the next 18 years. From a very basic evolutionary perspective, women need to be more careful.

This probably also accounts for why women value reliability in a man so highly. Even in today's age of economic equality, a woman is still at her most vulnerable when pregnant. A man who can be trusted to stand by her and support her is generally going to be considered a wiser choice. Some psychologists refer to this as "parental investment theory." This theory goes on to say that women are more likely to be attracted to a partner who offers financial and emotional stability than a man who is good-looking. Both would be nice!

Women have periods

Every woman is different, but for many women, periods are painful, intrusive, and very inconvenient. If, as a child, her family did not respond to periods in an accepting way, she may retreat at this time of the month. Or a woman might withdraw, simply because she feels unwell.

This physiological reality affects pretty much all women until menopause. Some may prefer to abstain from sex altogether during their period, while others limit themselves to certain sexual practices. It can also be the case that women just don't feel sexy at all and may not even like to be touched.

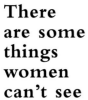

There are some things women can't see

Women's genitals are often a mystery. Not only to men, but also to themselves. The anatomical positioning of the female sex organs means that, unlike little boys, little girls are unlikely ever to see what's between their legs without the help of a mirror. Their privates are . . . well, private and hidden. Even in the showers, they're unlikely to see anything apart from blushes on their friends' faces.

Women also tend to be much less aware of sexual arousal. A man's excitement may be plain for all to see, but female arousal is more subtle. Consequently, it can be many years before a woman learns what's where, and what does what.

The A–Z of sexy "spots"

Heard of the G-spot? But what about the A, P, U, or X-spot? All of these have been identified by the popular press and amateur sexologists as erogenous areas. By this time next year they may have discovered the rest of the alphabet.

* *The P-spot:* This refers to the area just below the clitoris, surrounding the urethral opening, extending to the top of the vagina.

* *The U-spot:* This is similar to the P-spot, but specifically pinpoints the sensitive opening of the urethra.

* *The G-spot:* Some women say their G-spot, on the interior wall of the vagina, is highly erogenous; others find it uncomfortable to touch and still others say they don't have one. Scientists are still debating what the G-spot actually is.

* *The X-spot:* This is probably the most disputed one, but some women say that stimulation of the cervix during intercourse heightens arousal and can produce a really deep, satisfying orgasm. Other women say ouch!

* *The A-spot:* According to media sexperts, this is on the front vaginal wall, between your cervix and G-spot and it is about the size of a dime, and is smooth and sensitive.

Sex therapists recommend this exercise to help couples learn more about female anatomy without having to feel like a gynaecologist.

Start by both having a relaxing bath so your feeling clean and relaxed.

Sit up in bed, man with his back against the headboard; woman with her back against his chest. Prop a mirror on a pillow between her legs. Both of you can explore the reflection in the mirror. Either she can give you a guided tour or you can explore and ask questions. Make sure you take the time to check out the erogenous zones, touching the real thing now and finding out what feels good and what feels best.

Hormones and moody mysteries

Women look different from men because they're made of different chemicals. The key hormone responsible for femaleness is estrogen. Estrogen has been described as the "chemical with cleavage." It is responsible for a woman's curves, the softness of her skin, and the primitive scent that attracts a mate. It also has anti-depressant qualities and stabilizes mood. Estrogen is the key player in the chemical cocktail that accounts for female sexual desire.

Women also have testosterone, the chemical responsible for male sex drive, but in much lower quantities. Unlike testosterone, which actively and enthusiastically pursues sex, estrogen is much more laid-back and seductive. Estrogen is responsible for what has become known as female "responsive" desire. It encourages women to seek out an attractive mate, and then makes her available and willing. That's not to say that women's sex drive is passive. On the contrary, estrogen can be just as purposeful as testosterone, but rather than overtly express its desire, it will covertly and subtly seduce until it gets what it wants.

Unfortunately there's another highly influential component of the sex cocktail – progesterone. This hormone fluctuates significantly during the menstrual cycle, and when it is mixed with other chemicals, can put a women's sex drive into reverse. In fact, progesterone can have such a powerfully negative effect on sex drive that it has been used to chemically castrate sex offenders. Progesterone also promotes nurturing behavior, and, rather confusingly, also causes irritability and depression.

A different drink every day

Unlike the chemical cocktail flowing around the male body and brain, which pretty much stays constant throughout the years, women are more complex and changeable. The female cocktail works with the menstrual period over about 28 days and is different every single day. These constant changes affect women physically, emotionally, and sexually.

Although every woman is different, these are the common themes to be aware of:

❋ *First two weeks after a period:* Estrogen is high and women are at their most flirtatious and seductive. This is when the sex kitten comes out to play. General mood is positive, warm, and inviting.

❋ *Two or three days of ovulation:* Estrogen is high and testosterone peaks. Desire for sex will be strong and a little more aggressive than usual. The main sexual drive is for penetration and mood continues to be mostly positive.

❋ *The next 10 days:* Progesterone is high and during this time of the month a woman is more likely to want a cuddle than sex. The touching, nurturing nature of progesterone is dominant, and with lower estrogen and testosterone, desire for sex is at its lowest.

❋ *Premenstrual days:* Progesterone drops and testosterone has more room to flex its muscles. Sex drive may be most aggressive, but, unlike during ovulation, desire may be more for orgasm rather than penetration. Masturbation may be favored over partner sex.

❋ *Menstruation:* Progesterone drops even more, and for many women this brings relief. As estrogen and testosterone begin to rise, sex drive becomes more responsive, and the cycle begins again.

Reasons for having sex

What this all adds up to is that women often have complex and varying reasons for wanting sex. Like men, sometimes sex will be motivated by horniness. But at other times a woman may want sex because she wants to feel close. And at other times, because she wants to show love for her partner.

Orgasm is, of course, a significant incentive for many women, but certainly not for all. While most women enjoy orgasms, they're often not the be all and end all of sex. Some women are multi-orgasmic and can reach orgasm with minimal stimulation, while others prefer just one orgasm and are more leisurely about getting there. According to research, some women ejaculate, but most don't. All women are different.

Myths and messages

Throughout history, female sexuality has been alternately glorified and exalted, or degraded and abused. Perhaps one of the reasons for this is that for women, sex is a commodity. Whether it's trading for money, a promotion, or even personal

"It was only after living with my current partner for a year that I realized how my sex drive changes significantly through my cycle. Halfway through my cycle I can't get enough, but the week before I get my period, Sam reckons I give him the cold shoulder consistently."

ALICE, 26

safety, sex is a seen as a bargaining chip. Women have
something men want. In every culture in the world, you can
see women using the offer of sex to trade and bargain, but
rarely men.

This unspoken rule has, for many years, generated myths
about female sexuality that aim to control women's power,
often through guilt and shame. In a more recent reaction to this
sexual oppression, modern myths have evolved that promote
female sexual expression and performance. But often these
leave women with more feelings of anxiety, rather than fewer.

Old and new myths versus reality

❋ **Old myth:** Nice girls don't touch themselves.

❋ **New myth:** Liberated women masturbate regularly and love vibrators.

❋ **Reality:** Masturbation can be both relaxing and exciting and some women like the sensation of a vibrator. It also provides a safe arena to explore and experiment. But for many women, it's just not as good as partner sex and so they'd rather not bother – and that's fine too.

❋ **Old myth:** Ladylike women don't enjoy sex, and if they do, they enjoy it quietly.

❋ **New myth:** All women should be highly sexually responsive, multi-orgasmic, and enjoy a variety of different types of orgasm. If she's not able to pant and scream, she's probably inhibited.

❋ **Reality:** No matter how much of a sex god her partner may be, there will be times when a woman's body just doesn't want sex. For many women, enjoying sex is not dependent on having an orgasm. She may have one; she may not. Every woman's experience of orgasm will be different and there is no right or wrong.

❋ **Old myth:** Dressing sexily is cheap, tasteless, and asking for trouble.

❋ **New myth:** If you've got it, you should flaunt it.

❋ **Reality:** "Sexy" means different things to different people and is much more dependent on how we feel on the inside than how we look on the outside. And no matter who she is or what she wears, no one has the right to do anything sexual to her that she doesn't want them to do.

* **Old myth:** Women don't need to know anything about sex; a man should be in charge.
* **New myth:** Men need to be told what to do in bed, so it's a woman's responsibility to know what she likes. She should also make sure she's up-to-date with the latest tips and techniques for pleasing him.
* **Reality:** Most couples find sexual fulfilment through taking mutual responsibility for their sexual relationship. One or the other may sometimes take a dominant role in bed, but this is mutually agreed.

* **Old myth:** Most women don't like erotica in any shape or form; those who do are either promiscuous or perverse.
* **New myth:** She's frigid if she doesn't enjoy porn, erotic stories, dirty talking, and sex toys. And if she doesn't have an active fantasy life, she should work on getting one.
* **Reality:** It's all down to personal taste; there's no right or wrong. A genuinely liberated woman will feel free to experiment, but also confident enough to say "no thanks."

* **Old myth:** Men and women's experience of sex is totally different.
* **New myth:** Men and women's experience of sex should be exactly the same.
* **Reality:** *Everybody* is different.

How to turn her on – and off

If you're a man and you're reading this section because you want to find a sure-fire way of getting your woman in the mood, forget it. Unfortunately, no such thing exists. However, all this extra understanding and a few tips will hopefully help you to increase your success rate.

You need to remember that to turn your woman on you need to appeal to her heart, her head, and her body. Now that may seem like an impossible feat, but if you break it down, you'll see it's really quite straightforward. Most women in a committed relationship will agree that it's the emotional aspect of sex that needs to be addressed first. So . . .

Appeal to her heart

First and foremost this means she needs to know that she is cared for and valued. Women don't like to be seen *purely* as a sex object, they want to be a friend and a partner too: someone that you want to share your life – not just bodily fluids – with. This means you need to:

Talk about your feelings: Discuss your hopes and your fears in life and ask her about hers.
Support her: If she's going though difficult times, support her. And tell her that you appreciate her support when you are.
Be thoughtful and caring every day: Help out and be sensitive at every opportunity.

Show you enjoy being with her: Be physically affectionate, hold hands, hug, and kiss.

Tell her you love her: Something that's often overlooked when you've been together a long time.

Appeal to her head

Once you've got her heart in tune with yours, you need to think about what's going on inside her head. Being connected at an intellectual level is almost as important as the emotional stuff. Consider the following:

Check out her day: Ask about her day and tell her about yours.

Maintain the art of conversation: Keep up-to-date with current affairs and show interest in her opinions.

Find things to laugh about together: Not only is laughing fun but it's also stimulating.

Show you respect her: Clear up after yourself and share the workload around the house.

Ask her opinion: Find out what she thinks about different sexual practices and erotica, and show her that you're interested in her opinions about sex, not just her performance.

Be confident when talking about sexual desires: Women like men who know their own mind.

Pay compliments: Make it really clear how wonderful you think she is.

Appeal to her body

For many men, this might be where they would want a woman to start, but it's the other way round for us. Yes, the physical side of the relationship is important, but if the heart and head aren't in sync, the bodies won't be either. So, finally:

Look after yourself: A man who has let himself go is not generally considered sexually attractive.

Dress well: Don't wear anything you wouldn't want to be seen in on a first date.

Be clean: Be scrupulous with personal hygiene.

Act with decorum: If you have to fart or belch in your partner's company, be discreet.

Show you appreciate her body: Look, savor, and compliment.

Pamper her physically: Run the bath for her, rub her feet, buy her scent, massage her neck, stroke her hair – anything that says, "I love touching you."

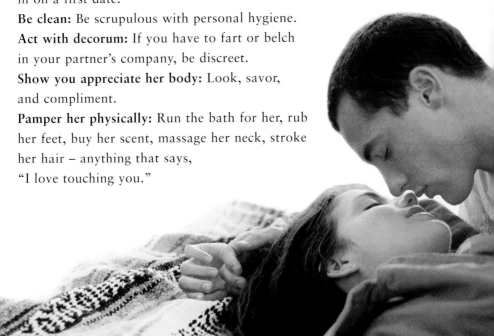

WHAT'S SO SPECIAL ABOUT MEN?

In today's world, in spite of a premium placed on everyone being equal, a big difference will always remain between what it means to be male or female. Male and female bodies, the way they function, and the roles and expectations assigned to gender by society are at the basis of a person's being. In Chapter 2 we explored what is special about women. We can now focus on men. You may be surprised by what we say.

3

Living with a penis

"It's a boy!" When the parents of a newborn child learn that they have a son, it sets in motion a whole set of feeling and cultural expectations – just because he has a penis. These expectations will shape the future of the boy and will be in direct response to his maleness. His role in society is assigned.

In many cultures the penis is the symbol of male power and authority. It goes beyond being able to produce children. For a man, having a healthy sexually functioning penis is part of the meaning of maleness. Yet today, where there is growing acceptance of the equality between the sexes, automatic male authority and power is being questioned. It used to be easier in the good old days. Or was it?

Regardless of social trends about gender equality, men have a special relationship with their penis. It is always there to remind him that he is male. Throughout his life, he will handle it a number of times a day, if only to urinate. How many times will a boy be told not to "touch himself" in public! Is he doing it just to remind himself that it is there, or just because it feels good? And why is it that athletes often seem to be absentmindedly poking and prodding themselves in their private parts, even when they know they're on national television? Reassurance or telling others that he has one too? By contrast, how many women are comfortable with touching themselves "down there"?

In both locker rooms and public places he can be confronted with the penis of other males, providing him with an opportunity of comparison or reassurance, or perhaps shameful self-doubt. Do women compare their bodies like this? Even if they do, it is more likely for form than for function. And of course, what will his sex partner think the first time they see it/him? Will it/he pass the test? Can he get it up when he should? What if he doesn't? Faced with these stresses, he might even think that women have it easy.

"My girlfriend didn't realize that my automatic sexual response surprises even me."

JOHN, 21

Erections, erections

We know that baby boys already have erections while in their mother's womb. Anyone who has changed a baby boy's diaper has seen the "automatic" erections with which he greets the world. And so it goes for the rest of a male's life. In fact, males experience erections throughout their lives during a phase of deep sleep called REM sleep. These nocturnal erections occur every 90 minutes or so throughout the night, but may diminish in frequency and intensity with aging. Men are aware of waking with an erection during the night or in the morning. The erections are part of the REM sleep cycle, and can even be accompanied by erotic dreams. However, many men attribute these erections to the need to urinate.

Nature gives men nocturnal erections to periodically keep the erectile tissue healthy and engorged with blood, to ensure the system is working and supplied with oxygenated blood. Women often wonder why an innocent hug or just quiet cuddling can so easily arouse a guy. It's not his fault – but nor is it the woman's. He is programmed that way. Of course many women later complain when his penis does not respond to him. A guy can't win.

SHE SAYS

Let's make things better, then make love.

HE SAYS

Let's have sex and make things better.

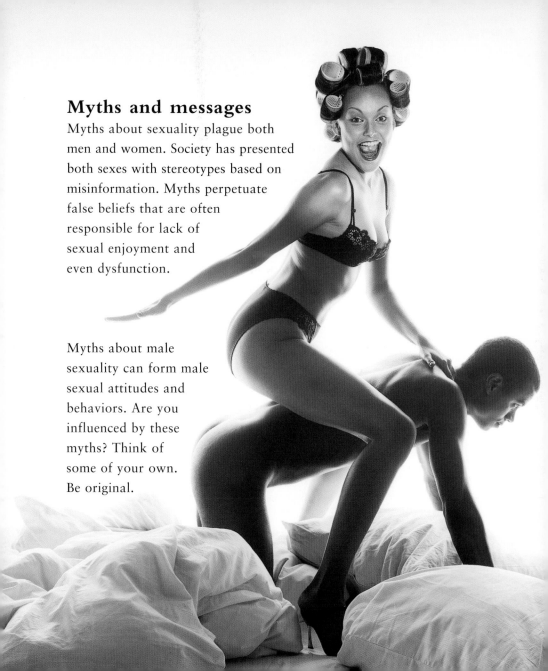

Myths and messages

Myths about sexuality plague both
men and women. Society has presented
both sexes with stereotypes based on
misinformation. Myths perpetuate
false beliefs that are often
responsible for lack of
sexual enjoyment and
even dysfunction.

Myths about male
sexuality can form male
sexual attitudes and
behaviors. Are you
influenced by these
myths? Think of
some of your own.
Be original.

Myths versus reality

* **Myth:** A man must always be ready for sex.
* **Reality:** Now that is looking for trouble. Who says so? Being too tired or not interested in sex at a given time is just a part of life – for both sexes. Trying to be sexual when he is not in the mood is an invitation to either sexual frustration, failure, or just a lousy time. No one wins.

* **Myth:** It takes a good erection to be a good lover.
* **Reality:** Erections are nice, but not always necessary to satisfy a partner. If a man knows how to please a partner with stimulation, caresses, and kisses to their favorite spots he'll bring her plenty of joy and satisfaction. In fact, rushing to intercourse even with a good erection can leave a partner unsatisfied because of a lack of attention to the pleasures of "outercourse."

* **Myth:** Giving your partner an orgasm is what being a man is all about.
* **Reality:** Now that is really putting pressure on a guy. Again, orgasms are nice, but not necessary. Many women are sexually satisfied without having an orgasm during sex. In fact, many women do not regularly have orgasms during intercourse, but can in other ways. For them, it is the pleasure of an attentive and caring lover that hits the spot.

Myth: Talking about sexual feeling is for women, not men.

Reality: It is the other way around. Being able to talk about sexual wants and desires with a partner is part of a good sexual relationship. So many couples have sexual difficulties *because* the men don't talk about what is happening. Partners are not mind readers. Speak up!

Myth: If you are having sex, there is no need to masturbate.

Reality: Poor masturbation. This is just one more myth about it. Self-pleasuring is part of the continuum of sexual behavior for both women and men, and is separate from intercourse. Who knows how to please a body better than its owner? The fact that a man enjoys masturbation in addition to intercourse is an individual matter and not in itself a sign of dissatisfaction or unmanliness. Many partners bring their awareness of what turns them on into their lovemaking. Then both partners benefit.

Myth: Porn and erotica are for men only.

Reality: Explicit adult erotica can be a turn-on for women too. Many women are regular visitors to online porn sites. Surprise! Some women, of course, have their own myths that nice girls don't enjoy that stuff (see page 39). It is a matter of taste and level of comfort. There are many sexually explicit and educational videos available for couples to enjoy. Sex therapists have been recommending them for years. See for yourself.

Male hormones: Do they ever quit?

Ask a man about his sex drive and he may talk about being at the mercy of testosterone. It makes a convenient excuse when women complain about men having sex on the brain.

Actually, the level of male hormone does decline with age (not quite a male menopause) and the hormone level does fluctuate in a daily rhythm (it is higher in the morning). But there are many years of living to do before the intensity of desire starts to wane.

There are several types of male and female hormones; it is just that testosterone and estrogen seem to get most of our attention. In fact, both the male and female brain are exposed to male hormones when in the womb. Males just have more exposure. And both males and females produce testosterone in the gonads (testes for males, ovaries for females) and the adrenal glands. Men simply have more. What is more, get ready: female hormones are even derived from testosterone – in both sexes. In this case it is the male who has less female hormones. But you knew that.

If women have testosterone too, what is the big deal about testosterone and men? Simply put, more is different.

"I used to be conflicted about what I now understand to be natural and healthy sexual feelings. Thank you, Mother Nature."

HARRY, 22

Testosterone is responsible for much of male drive, both sexual and aggressive, as well as mating behavior. As far as sex goes, testosterone is the desire hormone – in both sexes.

Since adolescent and adult males have so much testosterone in their system, a male's sexual behavior seems to be less cooperative than females to the restrictions of society. Hence the stereotype that "boys will be boys." This does not mean that males cannot or should not be accountable for their sexual behavior. Testosterone is present in boys before and since birth, but it is during puberty that male testosterone levels increase and are responsible for adolescent body and genital development, sperm production (wet dreams can be a surprise), increase in sexual fantasies, and preoccupation with sexual matters.

Let us not forget those often unwanted and embarrassing erections. "Where did that come from? I wasn't even thinking about sex." Discovering the pleasure of masturbation, ejaculation, and orgasm is a normal developmental enfolding during this time. However, there are many sex-negative attitudes in society that, while perhaps well intended, are likely to cause a lot of guilt and anxiety about how a young person experiences their emerging sexuality. Think about the messages concerning sex that you got from home or the Church. Some would say the message was "sex is dirty: save it for someone you love." How have early messages about sexuality influenced you? For some men and women, early sex-negative messages follow them even into their marital years, and can in part be responsible for later sexual problems.

The "tyranny" of testosterone (it isn't that bad, is it?) does diminish with age when a man's testosterone level begins to decline. This "andropause" is not quite the male equivalent of female menopause, because it does not interfere with reproduction. Some aging men who complain of anxiety, depression, loss of energy, and insomnia may find that a visit to the doctor for a testosterone boost may make their day. If there are no medical concerns to the contrary, proving middle aged men with testosterone replacement therapy, while not a routine, is making a come back. The feelings of some women about this "medical advance" have yet to be heard. I am sure it will range from "thank God" to "oh no!"

Why men often fall asleep after orgasm

Men report feeling spent, relaxed, and even sleepy after having an orgasm. This is mostly likely because of the release of neurochemicals during sexual activity and orgasm. However, this contented post-orgasmic experience is not always understood and appreciated by a sexual partner. While it is nothing personal, women don't always see it that way. Right?

Satisfaction: The importance of subjective experience

Here we are not talking about biological functioning, but rather a man's (and his partner's) emotional response to a sexual experience. Was it good, worthwhile, or great? If not, what got in the way? Were expectations about performance of either partner unrealistic? Was there "trouble performing" by either partner? The current outlook stressed by sex therapists is for partners to focus on pleasure, mutuality, and communication, rather than strictly on "performance." Emphasis is so often placed on performance during intercourse to the exclusion and neglect of the joy and pleasures of "outercourse" – the many sexual activities partners can enjoy apart from having intercourse. Outercourse is pleasure-directed, rather than goal-directed, sexual activity. In other words, with no goals to pursue, partners can just have a good time. Try it and see for yourself.

Using the term "foreplay" suggests that it must lead up to something else. Intercourse then becomes a goal rather than a part of being sexual. Good sex is what you and your partner feel good about. It is OK to leave the "experts" out of your bedroom (even us!). Enjoy yourselves, and remember, sexual satisfaction is a subjective experience.

"It took quite a bit of time to convince my husband that I didn't have to have an orgasm during sex to be satisfied. Finally he heard me. Now we both feel good about our lovemaking."

AUDREY, 40

Are men really so different?

Despite the apparent complexities, men and women are very much alike. While the process of raising male and female children varies greatly, both sexes are encouraged to establish relationships. Now here is when things get complicated.

In general, we know women are much better at establishing and maintaining relationships. Not only are females raised that way, but they seem to have an instinct for bonding. Men are different. Guys have buddies. They hang out but often don't do too much real sharing. In fact, males may often not know how they think and feel about some things or be able to express themselves. It is tough being raised as a guy.

But women know that men have feelings too. Ask a woman about dealing with a jealous boyfriend and she will tell you about male feelings.

How to turn him on

Many women complain that their partners are too easily turned on. But it's not unusual for the stresses of life to affect a couple's sex life. Here's some advice for getting your man back on track or, if you're lucky, just keeping him there.

Talk: He's not a mind-reader

Communicate better about sex! Sounds familiar, doesn't it? Feeling free to talk about what you like and want sexually really clears the air and turns him on. He's not a mind-reader.

Explore your sexual scripts

How can your repertoire be expanded for mutual enjoyment? This may include watching some porn together and discussing what one found sexy or unsexy about it. It will make him feel accepted too. But be careful about trespassing into too private a male domain. Some men are uncomfortable about sharing their "guilty pleasures."

How to encourage the shy guy

Look through a sexy lingerie catalog together and have him tell you what he likes about the model's bodies as well as

what they are – or are not – wearing. Hearing your comments helps him to see you in a sexier light.

Want to tease him?

Make erotic promises. You can really light a fire with a few words about looking forward to a sexy time together, or by responding to his touch by telling him it feels so good that he had better watch out.

When it comes to touch, more is better

Little touches and hugs go a long way in keeping his desire on the front burner. And getting a video on sensual massage for the two of you to enjoy – now that's another thing!

Sex toys, anyone?

They are mainstream these days and are not just for "kinky" people. A grown-up toy for him from you will go a long way.

Do you really know what you like?

Learn more about pleasuring yourself and what turns you on.

Let him see you turned on

It is very arousing for him to see you really turned on. Being able to let yourself go when you are with him is very, very sexy. He can't ask for more than that.

GETTING IT
TOGETHER

Many couples have mediocre sex lives because they can't get it together. Each blames the other for never being in the mood, but in reality, they're often both in the mood but don't know how to share it. Each and every day we are sexual beings and if we can keep connected with our partner, it is a smooth transition into seduction and arousal. The sexual engine is ticking over, ready to be revved up when the occasion arises.

4

Maintaining a sexual connection

If you want to have more frequent and better sex, then you need to connect sexually on a regular basis. Maintaining a sexual connection with your partner means being open and comfortable with sexual and erotic feelings. It means being able to communicate those feelings both verbally and non-verbally. Think of it as foreplay for daily life.

This kind of foreplay includes not only sensuality and romance as we talked about before in Chapter 1, but also the words, looks, and caresses. They might include:

- A lingering look or brief tough of breasts, bottom, or genitals that anyone but you would get chastised for.
- Any comment that overtly or covertly says, "I fancy you."
- A text message that says, "Thinking of you naked" or "Last night was great" or similar.
- A wink: old-fashioned but still profoundly intimate.

Sex talk

Maintaining a sexual connection also means being able to talk openly and honestly about sex. For many people, talking frankly about their sexual desires is awkward, or even embarrassing, but like all skills, it's something that gets easier with practice.

So many misunderstandings can happen when couples don't talk about sex: assumptions are made and frustrations and annoyances build up that could disappear instantly if only a couple would talk. It takes courage and commitment to talk openly about your sex life, but however difficult it might seem, it's well worth the effort.

Maybe you want to talk about how sex is initiated or about a particular stimulation technique you're enjoying or not enjoying. Perhaps you'd like to discuss trying something new. Whatever the case, tact and timing are essential. Make sure you choose a time and place where you won't be disturbed and both of you are feeling relaxed. Think through what you would like to say and make sure you are open to having a discussion and are willing to hear your partner's views too.

Most couples find that the best time to have this sort of discussion is not just before sex or in the heat of the moment. In fact, it's often best to keep the discussion to a time when you're both fully dressed and have time to think about what's been said before being sexual.

If you want to introduce a new idea, make sure that the decision is mutual and that you're not being critical of the status quo. For example, saying, "I would like us to learn some more ways that we can please each other," is much better than, "I want you to start doing it like this."

Case Story: *Gita and Sanjay*

Gita was scared that her husband of 16 years was having an affair. He had become increasingly distant and she wondered if he really was spending all his time at work. She was tearful as she explained to the therapist, "It's all my fault. Our sex life is non-existent and no one would blame him if he was going somewhere else."

The counselor explored what was happening in their relationship and it seemed that they lived like strangers. Gita was absorbed with the children and Sanjay was always at work. He asked Gita if she thought her husband would come with her to try and resolve their problem. Sanjay was reluctant at first. He told the therapist, "It's probably too late for us now. Gita only wants me as a provider for our family. I've always loved her, but the sexual side of our relationship seems totally unimportant to her." Gita was angry. It seemed to her that Sanjay just wanted a mother for his children. He showed very little interest in other aspects of her life and always put his job first.

The therapist helped each of them to let go of the resentment that had grown between them and they began to get to know each other again. They had to work hard at making time for themselves as a couple, to laugh and talk, and share their dreams for the future. As they reconnected they instinctively became more affectionate with each other. The therapist continued to work with them to help them to talk about their sexual needs and gradually rekindle the passion that was in both of them.

Seduction

You're connected emotionally and sexually – now you need to make it happen. The techniques for seduction are similar to those used for romance. But the motivation is very different. Romance says, "I love you." Sexual connection says, "We're sexual." Seduction says, "I want you *now*."

That doesn't necessarily mean that seduction only happens just before a sexual encounter. You may be in the mood all day and want to let your partner know. There are plenty of ways you can say, "Tonight's the night." You can pick up the phone, send texts, email, chat online, or simply slip a note into their pocket as they're leaving for the day.

The rules of seduction

Think about the style of your approach. What do you think is most likely to turn your partner on? What have they enjoyed in the past? What are you in the mood for right now? The style of approach you choose will probably influence the type of sex you'll have. So what takes your fancy?

* *Tender and romantic:* Maybe you'll start with a candle-lit dinner, massage, or foot rub, or anything tender and caring that says, "I love you." Perhaps even the dirty dishes!

* *Bold and brazen:* Perhaps you just want to get straight to the point, "Do you want to have sex, darling?" If that's

too abrupt, perhaps simply, "You're sexy; I want you." Or slip your hand straight to their hot button and say, "Well?"

❋ *Quiet and frenzied:* You could start with a hug and kiss, and then speed up the tempo so the kiss becomes a French kiss and the hands wander frantically.

❋ *Daring and erotic:* This takes guts but if the timing is right it can be fantastic. You could let you partner find you sexily dressed and ready for action. Or naked. Or if you're really brave, perform a seductive strip.

Remember the gender difference

In general, men have higher sex drives than women and will want sex more often. Even if you had similar sex drives in the early days of your relationship, as time progresses a woman's drive usually drops more than her partner's. Think of sex as being like our appetite for food. Men need to eat a lot to be satisfied and they get hungry more quickly. This means that they're busy serving up a lavish meal when their partner only wants a snack. So men, if you want your woman to initiate sex more often, you'll have to give her the chance to get hungry.

When the answer is "no"

If you're the one saying "no," then say it respectfully and lovingly. If possible, say when would be a better time. Obviously you can't ever give a cast-iron promise, but if tomorrow or Saturday really would be better, then say so. Also, be ready to give a reason why you don't want sex and why another occasion would be better. Sexual rejection can be extremely painful, and without a reason, your partner may take it much more personally than is necessary. Explain that you love them and still find them sexually attractive, but because of "x, y, z" you're not in the mood today. Remember that your partner will not be able to turn off their sex drive immediately after you've said no. Even if you don't want intercourse, you could consider manual stimulation or holding them while they masturbate.

If you're the one who has been turned down, be graceful about it. Don't sulk or whinge or get angry. If you do, you're going to create problems for the future, with a partner who never wants to have sex with you or an unresponsive partner who has sex just for an easy life. If you're feeling sexually frustrated, then masturbate, and get on with the rest of the day. If you feel you're being rejected on a regular basis and this is becoming a real problem for you, arrange a time to sit down and talk to your partner about how you can work together to sort out what's going on.

Case Story: *Sally and Nick*

Sally (35) and Nick (38) were a typical busy career couple with two young children. The demands of daily living left little time for sex. And when they did do it, it was always rushed and over much too quickly.

Nick had always come faster than he would have liked, but in recent years it had got worse and worse. Eventually they agreed they would go and see a therapist because sex, when they finally found time to do it, was becoming less and less satisfying for both of them.

The therapist explained that the techniques couple usually employ for overcoming premature ejaculation, such as using distraction and reducing foreplay, actually make the problem worse. Sally and Nick were told that they needed to spend much more time touching and caressing each other so that Nick would become more tolerant to arousal and raise his orgasmic threshold.

Over the next few weeks they followed a treatment plan of sensual and erotic exercises and gradually Nick developed greater and greater control. They still don't have any more time for sex than before, but when they do, it's great!

Being good with your hands

Studies have shown that touch lowers blood pressure and releases natural opiates in the brain that are associated with relaxation and positive feelings. Human touch is a powerful force. It can comfort, support, protect, encourage, relax, and, of course, arouse.

The precise way we like to be touched is different for every individual, but one thing is universal. We like to be touched by someone who likes touching us. Therefore it is essential to make sure your partner knows that it gives you pleasure to give them pleasure.

Before we look at specific touching techniques, you need to establish a way of finding out exactly what kind of touch your partner prefers. The best way to do this is to ask for feedback.

Asking for feedback

Asking for feedback may sound very simple, but there are some essential guidelines to follow to ensure your questions are effective, not intrusive.

* *Ask specific questions:* Asking "is this nice?" is unlikely to be very helpful. The answer will probably be yes, but what you really want to know is "is this good enough?"

* *Ask closed questions:* To allow your partner to stay focussed on their sensations, rather than having to think

through a response, ask a question that requires just a one-word response. Questions such as "would you like me to be firmer or gentler?" are much better than "what pressure would you like me to use?"

Use scaling questions: Ultimately you want to know if your partner is getting more or less aroused. One way to achieve this is to establish a scaling system. For example, on a scale of 1 to 10, you might agree that 1 = nice and 10 = orgasmic. So if your partner is on 4, you can ask, "When I touch you like this, where are you?" If they respond with a 6, you know you're heading in the right direction. If they say 3, you need to change what you're doing.

Don't ever think that once you've done this once you'll know what to do in the future. Our bodies are incredibly complex and what sends you off the orgasm scale on Friday might only get you to level 3 the next day. This is particularly true for women, whose skin sensitivity and receptivity changes with the menstrual cycle. Therefore, asking for feedback is not a one-off event – it should be an integral part of your touching routine.

Giving a sensual massage

One of the most universally popular ways of unwinding and getting close to your partner is to give and receive a sensual massage. Before you start, make sure that you won't be disturbed and your nails are trimmed. Then take some time to prepare the room. Think about relaxing lighting and some soothing background music and make sure that the room is warm enough.

Once you're ready to begin your massage, warm some massage oil between your hands and spread evenly over your partner's body. Use whatever kind of touch and pressure feels good to your partner and ask for feedback on what you're doing and adjust your stroke and pressure accordingly. Keep your movements steady and rhythmical, and try to keep your hands in constant contact with your partner's skin when you move to different areas of the body. Smooth, continuous, predictable movements are more relaxing than random strokes.

Massage should never be thought of as an automatic road to sex. But if you're inadvertently stimulating your partner's erogenous zones, you'll probably find you're more than halfway there.

Erogenous zones

Discovering your partner's erogenous zones is great fun, and they'll almost certainly have far more fun than either of you thought. You'll almost certainly get a response from the obvious zones, such as genitals, breasts, and buttocks. And probably from inner thighs, hips, and lower abdomen. But how about the less-known ones? For example, the inner elbows, backs of knees, the tender bit of skin behind the ears, between toes and fingers, feet, back of the neck, and armpits. All of these places can be tantalizing if you use feedback to find the right kind of touch.

It's important to realize that there are huge variations in how erogenous something feels. Where "mmm, lovely" ends and "aagh, that makes me horny" starts is a thin and ever-moving line. One day an accidental caress on the neck might send erotic shivers down your spine, the next it can leave you cold.

SHE SAYS ♀ ♂ HE SAYS

Women produce different amounts of lube at different times of the month, so please don't rely on how wet I am as a guide to how turned-on I am. Sometimes I can be dripping and uninterested and at other times I'm dry and desperate.

Men really appreciate it when a woman tells them when they are providing pleasurable clitoral stimulation. Men need guidance, especially when they feel the rules keeps changing, and are lost as to what to do – or not do – to please their partner.

How to please a woman

Generally speaking, women prefer a gentler touch than men. Always start slowly and gently and then work up to firmer and faster strokes. Being too heavy-handed can be off-putting at best and downright painful at worst.

Begin by lovingly caressing your partners thighs, her belly, her buttocks, and her hips – in fact, any other erogenous zones you've discovered. When she begins to arch her back and open her legs, you'll know it's time to get more intimate.

Before going to the clitoris or vagina, run your fingers through, or gently tug, her pubic hair. Caress her pubic bone and do a few circuits of the outer labia. Remember, teasing, playful fingers, are always more popular than poking, grabbing ones.

The internal labia, clitoris, and vagina are very sensitive so it's a good idea always to use some lubrication. Following are some popular stimulation techniques. As you try them, check out what pressure and speed your partner enjoys.

* *The clitoral circle:* Put the flat of your finger directly onto the clitoris and make small circular movements. Some women prefer the sensation of two fingers with the clitoris nesting in the join, or three fingers where the middle one remains in contact with the clitoris while the other two caress around it.

❊ *The figure of 8:* Like the clitoral circle, this can use one, two, or three fingers but this time make a figure of 8 motion. The clitoris is stimulated at the crossover point as you circle the vulva and labia in one half of the 8, and then circle the clitoris in the other, smaller half.

❊ *Plucking:* With one finger, caress from the base of the clitoris close to the vagina and up toward the tip, making a plucking motion.

❊ *Rolling:* Roll the clitoris between finger and thumb, either over the clitoral hood or directly on the head of the clitoris.

❊ *The labia tug:* Form your fingers into a "V" and rub them rhythmically up and down the sides of the clitoris inside the outer labia. This is particularly good for women who find direct clitoral stimulation uncomfortable.

❊ *Fingering:* Some women love to feel something inside them as their clitoris is being stimulated. Start with one finger up to the knuckle, and if that feels good, try a second, or even a third. Try either a pumping in and out or circular motion. To stimulate the G-spot, insert either one or two fingers in your lover's aroused vagina and make a "come here" motion toward her stomach.

How to please a man

Men often like a much firmer touch than women and prefer a more direct genital approach. However, a little teasing still feels great.
Start by teasing and caressing around the buttocks, the inner thighs, the lower belly, and pubic hair, before meandering along the perineum and toward the testes and the penis.

When it comes to penile stimulation, most men agree that an unlubricated hand is good but a lubricated hand is out of this world. A bit of lube to the head of the penis adds sensitivity, and the hand can glide more smoothly up and down the shaft. There are lots of different ways of giving a man a hand job, but below are some of the most popular movements.

❋ *Pump:* Make an up-and-down motion, ensuring your movements are smooth, fluid, and continuous. But be gentle – don't try to rip it off, he can tell you if he wants you to go faster. Either use one hand, gripped around the penis with all five fingers in contact, or just make a ring with two or three fingers. Vary the sensation with length of stroke and hand positioning. Some men love to have the thumb or fingertips positioned so they caress the frenulum with each stroke, or around the rim of the glans.

❋ *Two-handed pump:* Similar to the pump, but with two hands. One stays gripped around the base, while the other pumps up and down as required.

❋ *Two hands up:* Use two hands, one after the other, stroking the penis in an upward direction only. Keep the movement continuous, so as one hand leaves the top of the penis, the other is already following behind.

❋ *Twister:* Work your hand all the way from the base of the shaft to the glans, making a gentle twisting action as you go.

❋ *Head twister:* Similar to the twister, but focus just two fingers, twisting as if taking the top off a bottle.

❋ *Testicle teasing:* Gently cradle or massage the testes.

❋ *Anal stimulation:* The anal region is loaded with sensitive nerve endings that respond to gentle stimulation. Just playing in this area with a lubricated finger or butt plug can be great. Massaging the prostate is another thing, which may or may not be pleasurable. Go slowly if you try.

Being good with your mouth

After the genitals, the lips are the most sensitive part of the body. They're stuffed with nerve endings and can give and receive hours of pleasure. The most obvious use of our mouth (other than eating and talking) is kissing. This popular pastime is used by most cultures as a greeting and sign of affection. But when lovers kiss, it takes on a whole new meaning. When couples first meet, kissing is often intense and provocative. But over time, it's often forgotten. Thankfully, it's something you can easily learn again.

Rediscovering kissing

The key to becoming a better kisser is to start gently and explore. If your partner reciprocates, then continue; if they draw back, then do something else. You could also try taking it in turns to let your partner lead and show you how they like to be kissed. Either way, explore some new or old techniques:

French kissing: The well-known favorite, where you use your tongue to explore your partner's lips and mouth. Start gently, and as they open up, gradually increase the depth and urgency of your exploration.

Nibble kisses: Very, very gently caress your partners lips and tongue with little bites – but remember, gently.

Suction kisses: Gently suck on your partner's lips or tongue, or teasingly draw the breath from their body, but make sure you stop before they turn blue!

Chicken kisses: This can be very sensual, and very tickly. Gently peck your lover over and over and over again, with tiny kisses.

Teasing kisses: Gently and teasingly kiss your partner on the cheeks, the chin, the eyelids, the nose – in fact anywhere but the mouth. It'll only be a matter of time before they pull you to their lips.

When you've mastered the art of sensual, seductive kissing, you might want to use your mouth to continue to explore other parts of your partner's anatomy.

Oral sex

Whether or not you enjoy oral sex is a matter of taste (sorry, unavoidable pun). Some people love it, some hate it. Some love giving but not receiving, some like to receive but not give. As a couple, you need to sit down and work out what is best for you and what compromises you are happy to make.

If oral sex does end up somewhere on your agenda, you need to remember the same basic principles as touching with your hands. Namely, you need to let your partner know that you're enjoying pleasing them and you need to ask for feedback. Obviously the latter is not so easy, since we all know that talking with your mouth full is rude. So when giving oral, you'll have to stop for a moment before asking what feels best.

For her

When you've finished lovingly and teasingly playing with the rest of her body, you can use same kind of techniques you did with your hands, but obviously with your tongue. The circular motion, the figure of 8, and plucking. Since the tongue is generally much softer than fingers, you'll probably find your lover can enjoy more direct clitoral stimulation. You can also add the following:

Flicking: You can use your tongue to flick up and down the clitoris. Some women prefer long, slow licks from the base of

the shaft to the head, others prefer a feather light speedy flick just on the head.

Sucking: Gently suck on the head of the clitoris and maybe even draw in some of the vulva as well. Make sure you're gentle and release the vacuum gradually.

Oral sex has the advantage of leaving you with two free hands. You can use one hand to splay your partner's lips open so you have easier access to the clitoris and reveal more from under the hood, and the other hand can be used to teasingly caress the vulva or vagina. His free hands may also be used for breast stimulation.

For him

Start slowly and teasingly. Kiss and lick his belly and inner thighs, then work toward his perineum, balls, and then finally, before he bursts with anticipation, his penis.

SHE SAYS	HE SAYS
Please, please, please, on behalf of all women: please shave regularly. Stubble rhythmically rubbed over any part of our bodies hurts – especially our genitals. If you hate shaving, grow a beard.	*Sometimes women get carried away while doing oral sex and can accidentally bite a guy or catch a tooth on his sensitive skin. Covering your teeth with your lips can avoid accidents.*

Pumping: Make sure your neck and throat are relaxed, and form an "O" with your lips firmly around his shaft. He can place a hand around the base of his penis to avoid too much entry into your mouth, if that helps. Move up and down, starting slowly and then increasing the tempo. Some men prefer for their partner to work just on the head of the penis.

Add hand: As well as having his penis in your mouth, some men love to feel your hand on the lower part of their penis as well. Some prefer for you to just continue firm pressure around the base, while others will love it if you allow a well-lubricated hand to follow the motion of your mouth.

Tongue massage: Use your tongue to massage round and round the head of the penis in firm, smooth, rhythmical circles. Or use your tongue to caress the sensitive frenulum. You can either do this with the flat of your tongue, the tip of your tongue, or the back of your tongue – ask your man which he prefers.

Humming: Some men absolutely love this while others find it unbearably ticklish. While your man's penis is in your mouth, begin to hum – or moan. They will feel the sensation reverberate through to their penis and go mad, either with delight or giggles!

WHEN TWO BECOME ONE

The act of intercourse is the closest two human beings can physically get to each other. It allows our bodies to merge into a single, synchronous, mutually pleasurable act. Perhaps that's why for some people, intercourse is often regarded as "proper sex," the grand finale of sexual experience, superior to any other sexual experience.

5

Coital choreography

The problem with seeing intercourse as the main goal of all
sexual behavior is that it can devalue the pleasure of other
forms of stimulation. Also, it means that some men feel that
they should wait for penetration before they come, and then
when they do, it's game over. And the many women who
don't reach orgasm through penetration (estimated to be over
50 percent), may be left feeling that they're second-class
sexual citizens.

One of the great joys of intercourse is simultaneous
stimulation. You can both be equally involved in the sexual
experience, giving and receiving at the same time. But be
aware that just because you're both being stimulated at the
same time doesn't mean you'll both get aroused at the same
speed. It also doesn't mean that you'll both be receiving the
optimum stimulation required for orgasm.

Some years ago the mutual orgasm became almost the
holy grail of good sex. But in reality, striving for perfectly
synchronized, mutually satisfying sex is like trying to pat your
head and rub your tummy at the same time. Concentrating on
giving your partner pleasure will often mean that you're
distracted from your own, so your own orgasm may be
weaker. And it also means you're not fully available to share
your partner's rising rapture and orgasm. It's the worst of
both worlds.

Body ratios

Some couples fit together naturally, while many others don't. Most books on sexual positions assume the former, and can leave couples wondering why they can't achieve even the simplest-looking position. The reason is you're a different shape and size than the perfectly anatomically matched couple in the photograph.

If your partner is tall and you're short, some positions will be impossible. And even if you can manage the contortion, you might wonder why you're snuggling your partner's ribcage rather than kissing as the couple in the picture are. And if your partner has a generous waistline, and your arms are normal length, the suggested position for simultaneous clitoral stimulation may be completely lost on you.

Another often forgotten factor is the size of a man's penis. If you're within the average range then you and your partner can probably enjoy most positions. But as some well-endowed men have discovered, contrary to folklore, their partner does not swoon with delight at their approaching member, but recoils in wincing terror. The positions that allow for deeper penetration may be ones that you'll have to avoid.

You need to discover for yourselves which positions work best for you as a couple. But please don't think that just because it looks good on the picture or promises a certain type of stimulation that it will work for you. Some of us just ain't made that way.

Thrusting issues

Fast thrusting is often associated with frenzied passion, whether it's deep or shallow, while slow thrusting can be more teasing and sensuous. Both can feel amazing.

Shallow thrusting allows the sensitive head of the penis to be in contact with the nerve-enriched lower third of the vagina. The outer third of the vagina is also tighter, and it can feel wonderful for both to feel the wider part of the coronal ridge against this area.

Deeper thrusting allows the whole penis to be caressed and the woman may also enjoy the benefit of having her clitoris caressed by his pubic bone.

You might like to try a combination of positions in one session that involve deep and shallow thrusting. Whatever position you find yourselves in, make sure you experiment and check what feels good for each other. It really is a case of different strokes for different folks.

TRY THIS NOW!

Try practicing new positions with your clothes on. A night of passion can easily be wrecked by a limb giving way or getting cramped. To avoid this, put an evening aside when you're not planning on having sex and experiment to your hearts' content.

Try some of the tricky positions and see how your bodies fit together. And while you're there, see how long you can really hold it for! If you do collapse, you can guarantee it will be in a fit of giggles rather than frustration.

Case story: *Jake and Sally*

Jake (28) and Sally (32) went for psychosexual therapy 14 months into their relationship. Sex had always been pretty good for both of them, but Jake had often experienced erection problems. He had no difficulty getting an erection, and when Sally masturbated him or gave him oral it was fine. But he often lost his erection when they attempted intercourse. At first they were managing about a 50 percent success rate, but over time, things had got much worse.

Sally explained, "I try really, really hard not to mind and to be encouraging but I can't help thinking it's because I don't turn him on enough." "And of course that makes it worse," said Jake. "I so badly don't want her to think it's her fault that I put even more pressure on myself and fail." Sally laughed. "Which of course makes me blame myself even more – we're doomed!" They knew they'd got themselves into a catch-22, but they didn't know how to get out.

Much to their amazement, the first thing the therapist did was to ban intercourse. After a few weeks, during which Jake and Sally worked on some masturbation exercises, both of them felt more confident that if Jake did lose his erection, he would get it back. Then the therapist said that they were allowed penetration but Jake wasn't allowed to thrust. As soon as he felt his erection subside he had to remove his penis. After a few frustrating times doing this the therapist said that when he began to feel his erection subside he could thrust. They finished therapy a few weeks later. Neither could really put their finger on at what point they overcame the problem. But they knew that they no longer worried if Jake's erection began to fade, and consequently, it rarely did.

Sexual positions

If you want a good reason why sex need never become boring, consider this. Apparently there are over 600 different sexual positions. That is, 600 different ways to put a penis into a vagina. Many of the 600 positions must be remarkably similar, and you would both need to be Olympic gymnasts to achieve some of them. But even if you can only manage half of these, that'll keep you busy more than five days a week for a year!

This book isn't big enough to look at all 600, but following are just a few to get you started. The position you choose will depend on the mood, the situation, and perhaps the resources available. Some positions are good if the man wants to be in charge, while others give the woman more control. See what you fancy. A word of caution: If you have any back or joint complaints, then go very carefully with any new position.

SHE SAYS ♀ ♂ HE SAYS

I do like penetration, don't get me wrong, but I don't think it should be the be all and end all of sex. For me I need clitoral stimulation to reach orgasm, so for pure sexual pleasure, intercourse just doesn't do it.

Most girlfriends I've been with really don't appreciate what hard work intercourse is. They're lying there enjoying themselves while I'm holding up my weight and thrusting away. I wish they'd realize that we get tired sometimes and would really appreciate rolling over and letting them do some work.

When he wants to lead

On top: Missionary or variation-on-missionary positions are probably the most popular and most regularly used of all. In this position a couple can have good eye contact, body ratios allowing, and the man has good control of the thrusting motion. Depending on the position of the woman's legs and the man's pelvis, the depth of thrust and sensations will vary.

From behind: This position, often referred to as "doggy style," is one of the best for stimulating the G-spot. The penis comes from a different angle and it stimulates the front vaginal wall where the G-spot lies. The man's hands can also be left free for stimulating the breasts and clitoris.

When she wants to be in charge

On top: Positions where the woman is on top are very popular with women. In this variation on woman-on-top, she has maximum control of thrusting and gets good stimulation of her G-spot. Men often like these positions because they can lie back and enjoy the view.

Sitting or standing: Sitting or standing positions are great for a quickie. But contrary to the urgent encounters you've seen in the movies up against the nearest wall, standing is one of the toughest positions to achieve. Your bodies need to be around the same height, and penetration tends to be quite shallow. Sitting is a great height equalizer and the woman has great control over the thrusting.

Anal

Some people think anal sex is the ultimate in liberated sexual pleasure, while others just think it's a pain in the arse. And then there are those who consider it distasteful in the extreme. In some countries and some states in the United States "sodomy" is illegal, and many religions frown upon it.

The reason some couples really get into anal sex is because the rectum is full of sensitive nerve endings. The male prostate is sensitive and men can also enjoy penetrating a women's rectum because it provides a snugger fit than the vagina. Some women also report having more powerful orgasms when their anus is stimulated. But anal is not for everyone and if one of you isn't into it, speak up and make sure your partner knows your boundaries.

Fingers first

The difference between anal ecstasy and anal agony is relaxation. Mother Nature designed the rectum for one-way traffic only and put the sphincter muscle there as gatekeeper. To enjoy anal sex, you need to work on relaxing that muscle. Remember also that the walls of the rectum do not lubricate and stretch in the same way as the vagina, so they're more susceptible to damage.

To begin to relax the muscle you need to start slowly and gently. When your partner is fully aroused, insert a clean and lubricated fingertip. If that's comfortable then you might do a little massage around the internal rim. Remember to be slow and gentle. If that's feeling good then you can slowly prod a little deeper and see if you can insert another finger. Take your time to find out what feels good and remember to ask for feedback to find out what your partner enjoys.

When you know your partner's fully relaxed and aroused, and a finger is going in easily, you might be ready to try something bigger.

Penile shapes

The golden rule continues to be to go gently and slowly. Make sure your penis, or other apparatus such as a dildo, is well lubricated. Don't immediately thrust. When it feels comfortable for the recipient, then you can thrust gently. Make sure you're checking with your partner what feels good. If you do begin to experience discomfort, then make sure you exit very slowly. A quick anal exit can be extremely painful.

A final point to remember is that good hygiene is essential. You should always use a condom for anal sex to avoid germs that could infect the prostate, and unless your sex toy is very easy to clean, you should also put a condom on that. Latex gloves can protect you from unwanted cross-contamination. It is also imperative that you don't go straight from anal to vaginal intercourse. The anus contains various forms of germs that can cause infections if they get anywhere else, so make sure you wash thoroughly first.

EXPANDING YOUR REPERTOIRE

Sex doesn't have to become boring, even in a long-term relationship. Sex comes in lots of different flavors: tender, romantic, erotic, playful, passionate, hot, intense. If your sex life is beginning to taste a bit bland, you need to think about adding some spice.

6

Spicing things up

We all know that variety is the spice of life. So it follows that routine is the road to boredom. Of course, no couple ever intends their sex life to become routine, but unfortunately it happens. The most common telltale sign is when sex happens in the same way, at the same time, in the same place. Thursday nights, after the news, in bed. Ten minutes caressing, quick bit of oral then intercourse. But just as routines can be easy to slip into, they're also fairly easy to get out of.

Resurrect the quickie

One of the best ways to get out of a rut is to resurrect the quickie. Try a quickie before work or before you go out for the evening. You probably won't want your entire sex life to be made up of quickies, but the occasional one can stop sex becoming predictable. Grab any opportunity!

Change the location

In the same way as we all know that sex doesn't have to be saved for bedtime, we also all know that sex doesn't always have to happen in bed. But it's another routine that many of us slip into. A great way to spice up your sex life is to change the scenery. Why not try the bath, the shower, on the sofa, on a dining room chair, in front of the fire, up against a door, or over the kitchen table? It'll probably force you to be more adventurous with sexual positions too. Or go alfresco in your backyard.

Change your technique

Some people mistakenly think that having an orgasm means good sex. It doesn't. There are earth-moving, knee-trembling, mind-blowingly fantastic orgasms. But there are also mundane ones. If you've been with your partner a long time, you may know exactly which buttons to press to get a reaction. But just for a change, try finding some new buttons.

Sometimes you'll have to stretch beyond your comfort zones. You might occasionally agree to do something new that you're not fully sure about. But this is where people in a long-term relationship come into their own. The extra trust and security means you don't have to fear rejection or embarrassment if it doesn't work out. You're both in this together and you're both committed to maintaining a mutually fulfilling sex life.

This might include trying some sex toys, some games (more in Chapter 7), or simply trying a new stimulation technique or sexual position. It really doesn't matter what you do, so long as you're not offending your partner and you're adding variety and interest.

TRY THIS NOW!

Get a piece of paper and divide it into three headings:

| OK | NOT OK | GIVE IT A GO |

With your partner, brainstorm all the sexual practices you can think of. Then mark down each thing under the appropriate heading. Hopefully the things under "OK" you're already regularly enjoying now and anything that's "not OK" for either of you is a no-no. Those under "give it a go" are open for experimentation.

Cut up this list so that each activity is on a separate piece of paper. Put the pieces of paper in an envelope in the bedside drawer – and resolve to pick something new to try every week.

Flights of fantasy

Erotic fantasies appear to be a universal part of the human sexual experience. They've been around for centuries, and regardless of age, gender, or culture, we all seem to fantasize about the same sorts of things. A rich fantasy life can have many benefits for a sexual relationship. It can add novelty to a sex life that is beginning to lose its spark; it can provide an arena to practice things alone, before trying with a partner; and it can be a useful way of blocking out anxious thoughts.

How we feel about our sexual fantasies will depend largely on our sexual attitudes, and also our sexual tastes. Some people feel comfortable talking about their fantasies, while others prefer to keep them private. Some may feel embarrassed or even ashamed.

Some example fantasies

* *Sex with a stranger:* Fantasizing about sex with a stranger gives the opportunity to experience the perfect sexual encounter with no strings attached. Since you don't know your fantasy stranger and will never see them again, you can enjoy sex for sex's sake with no pretence and no price to pay. The fantasized stranger will be perfect in every way and they'll be someone who sees you as being perfect in every way too.

* *Sex with someone famous:* Similar to sex with a stranger, fantasies about sex with an unobtainable, seemingly perfect person whom our society holds in high esteem is another common theme. People fantasize about having sex with all sorts of unlikely celebrities!

* *Sex with more than one person:* Many of us occasionally doubt whether or not we're able to sexually satisfy our partner. In these fantasies those doubts are well and truly alleviated. Imagining having sex with more than one person means being attractive enough, horny enough, and fit enough to satiate multiple appetites. This fantasy is thought to be more common among men.

- ❋ *"Rape" fantasies:* These are more common to women and it's essential to understand that the "rape" is always wanted and therefore not really rape at all. While the sex may be passionate and forceful, it's never painful or abusive. The emphasis is on being found so irresistibly attractive that the man just couldn't help himself. It's also thought that some women, who may have been brought up to think that being sexual is wrong, can relinquish responsibility for their arousal and allow themselves to enjoy sex without guilt.

- ❋ *Same-sex fantasies:* Each of us, to a lesser or greater degree, is attracted to people of our own gender at some stage in our lives, and same sex fantasies are the unconscious mind's way of experimenting with this other side of ourselves.

- ❋ *Watching and being watched:* Sex is meant to be a private affair. But many of us get excited by doing something that we know we're not really meant to do. Allowing ourselves to be seen while having sex, either out-of-doors or recording a video of our sexual exploit, or alternatively peeping on someone else means we're breaking the rules, and this can heighten the sexual experience.

Sharing sexual fantasies

Sharing a sexual fantasy involves a great degree of trust, because once something is told, it cannot be untold. If you and your partner share similar fantasies, then it's likely that sharing them will be a rewarding and enriching experience. But if your tastes are different, your disclosure could be met with an embarrassed silence, shock, or even disgust.

Sharing fantasies can be liberating – but only if they're accepted. If you think you'd like to share your fantasies, talk to your partner first about the general theme – then gradually continue, with caution.

Acting out fantasies

Should you or should you not act out a fantasy? Of course, there is no right or wrong answer to this. Some people have no desire to ever act out their fantasies while others long for the opportunity.

If you would like to act out a fantasy, then obviously your partner needs to be in agreement. Before you do, you need to consider how you'll feel if the fantasy doesn't live up to your expectations. The reason fantasies are so sexually arousing is because they are always perfect, but unfortunately, reality rarely is. Some people regret acting out their fantasies because it spoils them. The dream was not as good as they hoped and consequently the fantasy loses its sparkle forever.

Case Story: *Jon and Fiona*

One night, after enjoying lots of wine, Jon (29) and Fiona (25) began taking about sexual fantasies, particularly about former lovers. Jon felt comfortable enough to share that he still thought about his old girlfriend, Sarah, but assured Fiona that she was his only love.

Fiona was more resistant to sharing, but after Jon's urging, she admitted that she, from time to time, recalled good sexual times with an old boyfriend.

Jon was surprised that he had trouble hearing this. He became jealous and angry with Fiona. She regretted sharing with him. The couple eventually sought professional help.

The counselor told them that while many couples are able to share sexual fantasies and use them to enhance their sexuality, others are not able to hear their partner's "secrets." Jon and Fiona stayed together, but learnt a good lesson about the limits of personal privacy.

Tantric sex

The art of Tantric sex promises profound intimacy and sexual ecstasy. Tantric sex offers an alternative to goal-orientated, genital sex. According to Tantra, boredom sets in when people make love only with their genitals, not their hearts and minds. It strives for sexual union and sexual harmony.

The origins of sacred sex

Sacred sex started in India in 5000 BC through the cult of the Hindu god Shiva and the goddess Shakti. The Hindus believed that when these ancient gods united sexually and spiritually the universe was created. Therefore, lovemaking can generate the energy not only to create new life, but to create *all* life.

One of the ancient Eastern sciences of enlightenment was Tantra. Unlike most mystical paths, Tantra included sexuality as a doorway to ecstasy and enlightenment. The word Tantra means "weaving," unifying the many and often contradictory aspects of the self into one harmonious whole. It also means "expansion," in the sense that once our energies are woven together, we can grow and expand into ultimate ecstasy.

The Kama Sutra has become synonymous with sacred sex. Literally meaning "guide of the Hindu God of love," it is the earliest surviving example of a Hindu love-manual. The Kama Sutra was compiled by the Indian sage Vatsyayana, sometime between the second and fourth centuries, and is based on earlier manuals that go back 2,700 years.

The philosophy

Tantric philosophy, as with many other Eastern sciences, believes that our body has energy running through it in a similar way that blood runs through our veins. This energy connects the body's seven "chakras," or energy centers. It is believed that we can open up our chakras and move energy through these channels to create a sensation of wholeness and ecstasy.

Unlike most Western images of sex, which are energetic and urgent, Tantric sex is meditative and gentle. The essence is to be able to get in touch with your powerful sexual energy and learn to channel it through the seven chakras. When you feel the tension of sexual arousal building, you relax into it and spread it to the rest of your body. So rather than localized genital sensation, the experience of arousal is a full-body one.

At orgasm, rather than just a genital release, the whole body ripples with wavelike pulses. This is known as the full body orgasm. This full body orgasm is said to be "an altered state of consciousnesses." When two of you experience this together, the energy between your bodies melts and merges and you can enjoy complete sexual communion.

The practices

It is thought that inhibitions restrict and stifle sexual energy so it's essential to have a positive sexual self image in order to enjoy Tantric sex. Much emphasis is placed on self-esteem and taking time to be at peace with oneself and the world.

Sex is also an act that involves all the senses. Whether you're having sex alone or with a partner, time should be spent in reflective meditation to still the mind and body ready for love. The environment should be calm, warm, and inviting to all the senses through aromatherapy smells and candles. This is often referred to as the "sacred space."

Having created this space, there are many different ways to experience of the power of Tantra. These include:

Self-masturbation: As with every other form of Tantric sex, the aim of masturbation is to move beyond the focus on the genitals to a full body experience. Self-pleasuring is expanded so that as you reach the pinnacle of pleasure, rather than going for orgasm, you hold the tension, relax into the sensations, and send the energy through the chakras out into the body extremes. Controlled breathing and visualization are considered key skills for achieving this. Rather than holding your breath and trying to resist the power of the physical sensations, breathe through it, ride the sensations, and visualize them spreading from the genitals, up through your body. Continue to ride and expand each wave of pleasure until you're ready for the final release of the full body orgasm.

Masturbating together: Couples are encouraged to create their sacred space together and begin by connecting their energies. This is done by quietly focusing on honoring and respecting your partner as the other half of yourself. Once connected, you're ready to begin to share the Tantric experience. Again, it's considered essential to break through any inhibitions, and learning to masturbate in one another's presence is considered a good way of doing this.

Tantric lovers are encouraged to masturbate while holding each other's gaze in full-eye contact. This experience can empower them both. Each is able to take responsibility for their own sexual release and show how they like to be touched. They can also feel free from the pressure of thinking they are the sole source of their partner's pleasure.

Mutual masturbation: When stimulating each other, lovers are encouraged to maintain eye contact and communicate as they build their partner's sexual energy and expand it through the charkas. The Tantric couple learn to flow in tune with each other's energy and to ride ever-higher levels of arousal, before holding their partner as they relax into the sensations, before building up and riding again.

Sexual intercourse: There are many recommended positions in Tantric sex, most borrowed from the Kama Sutra. Some of the positions are quite simple, while others are aimed at people who are already proficient at yoga. The position that is widely considered the most powerfully intimate is the Yab Yum. Yab Yum means "mother and father union" and provides maximum physical contact and the opportunity to align the chakras of the body so that sexual energy can be shared.

This is a seated position where the woman sits on her partner's lap, facing him with her legs wrapped tightly around his waist. Both have their arms around each other. Without thrusting, the couple focuses on their individual sexual energy and expand it through the seven chakras in synchronicity as they melt into mutual sexual ecstasy. There is not enough space here to do justice to the power, potential, and intricacies of Tantric sex. If this is something you'd like to explore further, then invest in one of the many excellent books on the subject.

TRY THIS NOW!

You need to allow at least 10 minutes for this exercise when you will not be disturbed.

Start by sitting and facing your partner. Gaze gently into each other's eyes for a few moments and then bring the cupped palms of your hands together in front of you and rest your thumbs against your chest.

Close your eyes and, as you exhale, both of you should gently bend forward from the waist, keeping your back straight. Bend forward to a 45-degree angle until your foreheads lightly touch. Hold this connection for a few minutes, focusing on the openness and respect this gesture conveys.

When you're both ready, sit up straight, open your eyes, look into your partner's eyes and say, "[Name], I honor the god/goddess within you."

ADULT TOYS AND GROWN-UP GAMES

As well as being intimate and loving, sex should be fun and exciting. Injecting some toys and playful new games into your sexual relationship can add a new dimension and prevent boredom from creeping in.

7

Vibrators

Think of sex toys and you probably instantly think of
vibrators. The vibrator is by far the best-selling sex toy on
the market, available in a vast range of shapes and sizes. The
traditional penis shape is still popular, but now you'll find
shapes specifically for stimulating the clitoris, G-spot, and
general vulval region. But don't be fooled into thinking
they're just for girls. Many men enjoy the sensation of a
vibrator, too.

Anything to tickle your fancy

The sex toy market certainly doesn't end with vibrators. There
is an ever-expanding range of products, and with the Internet,
you don't even have to leave home to buy them. You might
want to buy your lover a little gift to remember you by or
something you can share together.

* *Artificial vaginas:* More evidence that vibrators
  aren't just for girls. The blow-up doll is also still alive
  and kicking, and a much better-crafted product than
  ever before.

* *Love balls:* As well as feeling great, these are good
  for strengthening a woman's pelvic floor muscles. Two
  small weighted balls are popped into the vagina to
  rock and roll.

* *Dildos:* Penis-shaped objects, known as dildos, have been around for 12,000 years. They come in a range of designs and sizes, or if you want, you can buy a molding kit and make your own.

* *Strap-ons:* A number of dildos are available with a harness known as a strap-on. The harness can be worn by either partner to penetrate the other. There are also double strap-ons that stimulate vaginally and anally, and double-ended strap-ons that stimulate the wearer at the same time as the partner.

* *Ticklers:* Available in a variety of materials, these are attachments for the penis that provide extra stimulation of the clitoris on penetration.

* *Butt plugs:* These are specifically designed for providing anal stimulation. They come in different sizes and shapes and all have a flanged end to ensure they don't get lost!

* *Novelty items:* What d'ya fancy? A cock-shaped candle, a nobby nail file, a dirty scrubber for the bath? You could buy your partner a sexy mug to keep them thinking of you throughout the day.

Case Story: *Jenni and Dom*

Jenni had never had an orgasm. At 28, she felt like the only woman in the world who hadn't "properly" enjoyed sex. She had faked orgasms to please boyfriends, but since meeting Dom, three months ago, she had vowed never to do so again. Dom was special and she wanted to be honest with him. So she told him her secret. He had been really supportive and said he'd do anything he could to help her overcome the problem.

Jenni plucked up courage to talk to her doctor. He asked a few basic questions and concluded that the problem was psychological. He referred her to sex therapy. The therapist told Jenni that her problem was extremely common. She asked about her background and explored any negative messages she might have about sex. On the whole, Jenni had a very positive view of sex and it seemed her problem was more likely due to inadequate stimulation. This was compounded by the fact that Jenni had never felt aroused enough to masturbate and therefore didn't know what kind of touch she enjoyed.

The therapist suggested a masturbatory plan to develop her self-awareness. Jenni was comfortable with the exercises but never felt aroused. The therapist suggested erotic fiction. At the next session, Jenni was delighted. "I've found the best book in the world, but now I have another problem. I get really turned on but as much as I stimulate myself, I don't seem to be able to reach orgasm." The therapist recommended some further stimulation – a vibrator. Two sessions later, Jenni had reached her goal. "So that's what it feels like," she laughed. Jenni's orgasmic response got stronger and faster and she never looked back.

Erotica

Whether something is erotic, pornographic, or offensive is a matter of personal taste. Society struggles with diverse opinions about erotica, ranging from the feminist anti-porn campaigners to the libertarians who see it as an expression of human rights. Erotica in different forms has been around since the dawn of time, when cavemen chiseled provocative images on their bedroom walls. Undoubtedly even then there were some who loved it and some who hated it.

Erotic literature

There is a huge range of erotic literature on the market, from short stories to epic novels, in book form or magazines. You might enjoy reading true stories, reader confessions, fantasies, or thriller. Or, of course, work your way through the lot! If you're too shy for your bookstore, jump on to the Internet.

"Introducing erotic materials into our sex life has opened up a whole new avenue of enjoyment and exploration. My partner was surprised how turned-on she could become. Before that, sex was getting routine and even boring. I'm glad she was willing to try these new things."

TONY, 50

Ear-otica

This is a fairly new addition for those of us who either don't have time to read or are vision-impaired. The range of audio stories is steadily growing, though it's not up to speed with the written word yet.

Magazines

Magazines are still one of the most easily accessible forms of erotic material and the range is vast. Obviously, you've got your top-shelf titles ranging from *Playboy* to titles which turn humble housewives into superstars. On the middle shelf you've got lad-mags like *Esquire*, and *Cosmopolitan* for the girls. If you feel uncomfortable buying something from a shop, then the Internet provides the perfect opportunity to subscribe online.

Art

Erotic art is the oldest form of erotica available. Some is subtle and discreet, some is set in a historic context, some is funny and humorous, and some is simply beautiful to look at. You can choose from photography or illustrations or sculpture. Styles include comic book, oriental, futuristic, period, and contemporary. You might have a selection of saucy postcards or one, very expensive, limited-edition print.

Sex on-screen

As you know, there are endless cable television channels dedicated to erotica of every different taste. If this doesn't take your fancy, head to your local rental store. Erotica that appeals to you might range from a raucous high-school romp to a romance with a few steamy sex scenes. And then, of course, you can work your way through the movies made to tease. If you find yourselves running out of choices at your local store, try the Internet.

Sharing

People use erotica in a variety of ways. Many like to read or look at images during masturbation, and others like to read or view things alone to get them in the mood for their partner. An increasing number of couples enjoy sharing erotica together. If this is something new to you as a couple and you feel a bit self-conscious, then start with something light. In fact, a good starting point could be reading this chapter together and discussing what you think. When you're both feeling comfortable, move on to something a little raunchier. Remember that it won't be erotic unless you're both enjoying it. So make sure you're open and honest with each other about how each experience affects you.

Sex games

In a long-term relationship, sex can become monotonous and mundane. And as the pressures and routines of daily life expand, it can sometimes be easy to forget about sex all together. Building sexual play into your entertainment agenda can help to keep the intimate side of your relationship at the forefront of your minds. So even though you're not having sex, you won't forget how much fun it is.

The choice of nonsense that couples can get up to in the name of saucy sex is limitless – here are just a few ideas you might like to try.

* *Play fights:* Whether it's wrestling on the sofa, pillows at dawn in the bedroom, or a water fight in the garden, get your adrenalin going with a friendly tussle. Not only will it get your heart beating faster, but it will also leave your body more responsive and easily aroused.

* *Nude chores:* Any daily routine can be made much more interesting if you get your clothes off. Whether you're doing your accounts, the housework, or cooking the evening meal (though you may need to be extra vigilant with the last one!).

* *Blind man's buff:* Losing the sense of sight often heightens other senses. Try blindfolding your partner and

teasing their body with different textures. Or give them objects to feel and identify. Choose items that have sexual connotations and add the occasional real, live body part.

❋ *Not-so-bored games:* You can sex-up pretty much any commercial game that you already have in the home. Everyone has heard of strip poker, but any game can have removing an item of clothing as the penalty for losing. Or try Scrabble where every word has to be rude, or Taboo or Pictionary, where the word you're trying to describe is something sexual.

❋ *Dicing with danger:* Get a pair of dice and assign one to six on one die with different body parts, and one to six on the other with different types of touch. Roll the dice and follow the instructions. Rolling a three might be a kiss, and a two a caress. Four might be the end of your nose, and two a nipple. You might want to reserve a double six for something really special . . .

❋ *Water fun:* The silky sensation of water and bath oils can make the skin feel beautifully sensual. Whether you're in the bath or shower, do spend some time rinsing each other down with the showerhead. If you've got a pulse option in your shower, you might find this particularly invigorating!

Dressing up

At the simplest level, dressing up might simply mean enjoying the sensual touch of silk, satin, lace, or leather next to your skin. Whether you prefer something pretty, something sophisticated, or something raunchy, there's a huge range of lingerie available for both sexes to enjoy.

As well as lingerie, many couples enjoy dressing up for role-play. You might fancy a game of Doctors and Nurses, Chambermaid, or Stripper. Some couples simply enjoy wearing the clothes, or rather taking them off, while others like to get fully into the role and build a sexual scenario to act out.

Bondage and S&M

Bondage and S&M are only erotic when they're enjoyed by two consenting people. It involves a high level of trust and absolute faith that a partner will stop if you feel uncomfortable. There are a range of practices that fall under the general headings of Bondage and S&M, beginning with a gentle spank or being lightly restrained, to bondage chambers and whips.

Light bondage

Many people enjoy being restrained lightly during sex play. Having your hands tied behind your back or tied to the bedposts forces you to be totally passive. You can focus purely on your own pleasure, as you couldn't stimulate your

partner even if you wanted to. For the person who's doing the tying down, the feelings of control and power can be delicious. You can tease and caress until your partner is begging you to stop. Or use their body for your own pleasure.

Taking turns to be tied down will give you both the chance to see how it feels in each role. But make sure that if either of you begins to feel uncomfortable at any stage, you stop.

Light spanking can be arousing for a number of reasons. The first is that it generates adrenalin, which heightens the body's responsiveness to stimulation. Endorphins are also released, one of natures feel-good chemicals and also a pain reliever. It is thought that this double release makes the combination of pain and sex enjoyable.

A succession of smacks on the rump send reverberating vibrations through the genital organs, so as long as there isn't too much of a sting to distract you, you'll be getting stimulated in more places than the obvious. But whatever you do, make sure smacking starts gently and builds up slowly. Forgetting your own strength and giving a painful wallop is a real passion wrecker.

In fact, experts in S&M never say no, just in case it's misunderstood. Serious practitioners have developed their own vocabulary. Saying "yellow" means slow down a bit, not quite so hard and saying "red" means stop now. You and your partner could agree to using these terms if you like, or think up something else. What's important is that you both know how to say "no" and mean it.

Heavy bondage and S&M

This is where the chains, leather, scarves, tickling feathers, and whips come in. The term Heavy Bondage is used to include Sado Masochism (S&M), Bondage & Discipline (B&D), and Dominance & Submission (D&S).

S&M: One person plays the dominant one and one person plays the submissive one. Some people prefer always to play the same role while others will swap round.

B&D: These are the scenarios that you read about in the tabloids involving politicians. One person is tied up and humiliated, physically punished, and disciplined.

D&S: A bit like S&M, but pain doesn't have to be involved. The person who is dominant (often called the Top) gives orders to the person who is submissive (the Bottom).

If you want to experiment with the heavy bondage scene, then definitely make sure you're both comfortable with the light end first. Then proceed slowly and with caution, and keep checking that both of you are still enjoying what you're doing.

A LIFETIME OF GREAT SEX

Research has also shown that couples who continue
to have an active sex life are more likely to keep
fit and age more slowly (or at least look as though
they are). An active sex life helps us to feel happy,
enhances the immune system, increases lean body
tissue, and thickens skin tissue. As if you needed
any more reasons to keep having sex . . .

8

Making babies

Sometimes we get so wrapped up in how good sex feels that we forget that it's also the way that babies are made. Whether you're trying to make babies, have just had one, or have growing children, your sex life will not be the same. Parenting takes an emotional and physical toll on any couple. Your relationship will move into a new era and so will your sex life.

Trying for a baby

When you're trying for a baby, sex takes on a new meaning. Not only are you enjoying physical pleasure and sharing intimate time together, you're also creating new life. For most couples this is an excellent excuse for having a lot more sex. But bearing in mind that it takes the average couple eight months to conceive, it's important that you don't make conception your raison d'être.

If you've been trying for a baby for over a year, then you may decide that it's time to see your doctor, who may refer you to a specialist. This can be a very difficult time for couples. Medical intervention can leave sex feeling very clinical, and fears of being told that one or both of you can't conceive can leave you wondering if sex is a futile activity. During this time, many couples find that sex feels like work. Try to remember that, as well as being the way to make babies, sex is also fun and has the power to comfort, relax, and soothe as you each go through this difficult time.

Sex during pregnancy

How couples feel about sex during pregnancy varies
enormously. For some it's a huge relief not to be trying for a
baby anymore and sex can now go back to being purely
recreational. For other couples, it can feel a bit strange. Now
there aren't just two of you making love – there are three.
Some couples prefer to check with their doctor about sex
during pregnancy, particularly if there has been a history of
miscarriage, while for others, it's business as usual.

Sex will feel different over the three stages of pregnancy. In
the first three months sex may feel pretty much the same as it
always used to, though unfortunately, many women are
plagued with nausea and tiredness. The next three months are
when most women begin to show, and while some feel
healthy, others feel self-conscious about their growing breasts

SHE SAYS ♀ ♂ HE SAYS

*My sex drive went through the roof when
we started trying for a baby, but as soon
as I got pregnant, it felt strange. Luckily
my husband and I were able to talk
things through and though we didn't
make love as much while I was pregnant,
when we did it was really special.*

*As soon as Julie announced she was
pregnant I wanted to make love. We'd
been trying for ages and that had made
us really close. She looked fantastic
throughout her pregnancy but it was
really hard because she rarely felt up to
having sex. I didn't want to hurt her but
I was so frustrated.*

and belly. In the final three months, the baby is going to be heading for full size and couples will need to become more creative with sexual positions. Many couples find that positions from the rear are most comfortable. Sexual desire may go down for men and women as the preparations for becoming a parent speed up.

Sex after childbirth

The first few weeks after a baby is born are often the most exhausting weeks of a couples' life. Whether you're breast-feeding or bottle-feeding, it's unlikely that your new born is going to sleep through the night. And for many couples, the sheer newness of the situation is tiring. There are so many extra things to consider. On top of the usual earning a living and maintaining a home, there are nappies, feeds, nursery rhymes, and hundreds of relatives to visit. As you're adjusting to the new role of parenting, sex can be one of the last things on your mind.

On top of this, 80 percent of new mothers report lowered sexual desire in the first few months. As well as exhaustion, this is due to hormonal changes. Knowing that the body needs to get back to full strength again and that all energy must be focused on the new baby, Mother Nature temporarily depletes the sex urge hormones to ensure that brothers and sisters don't arrive too soon.

During this time it is essential that couples keep talking to each other. Moms and dads can feel guilty about not wanting, or wanting, sex. Being able to share how you feel together and supporting each other in the early months will help you to maintain intimacy and your identity as a couple.

Whether you're ready to have sex again or not, and no matter how infrequent it may be over the coming months, remember that you are still lovers as well as parents.

When the kids are small

Finding time to have sex with a newborn baby in the house is difficult, and things will probably get worse before they get better. But before you despair, there are advantages. Whether you've just got one little bundle of joy, or a couple of toddlers bombing round the house, now's the time when your sex life can be at its most creative. If the two of you had begun to slip into any routines, having kids will force you out of them.

SHE SAYS ♀ ♂ HE SAYS

Obviously I didn't want sex for the first few weeks, but after that I was OK. I was always too tired at night but at weekends, when Aimee was sleeping, we were at it like rabbits.

I didn't really feel like sex after the baby was born, which surprised me. I expected her to be the one saying no, not me. I was just too exhausted and it took me a while to get used to being a dad and seeing her as a sexy woman, as well as a mom.

Sex at bedtime may well be a thing of the past, but don't be lulled into thinking you'll ever establish another regular time. Just when you've got into the habit of sex on Sunday afternoon, little Billy will decide he no longer needs a nap. And if first thing in the morning becomes your favorite time of day, darling Daisy will decide she wants to be awake to see the sunrise from now on.

Now is the time when you need to develop a balance between planned sexual marathons, average encounters, and passionate quickies.

If your kids are young enough, try to get them all into bed early so you still have time for some adult activities. But whatever you do, don't be tempted into spending the evening catching up on chores or sitting in front of the TV. If you want a nice, quiet dinner with some uninterrupted grown-up conversation, that's fine. But however you like to spend your evening, *have sex first*. Most people are shattered by the time they go to bed and are only fit for sleep. If you want to enjoy sex, put this as item number one on your evening agenda, and then do everything else.

Quickies are where you can be most creative. Become an expert at recognizing the opportunities. That could be nap times, when a friend comes round to play, when they're engrossed in the latest cartoon, or when grandma takes them to the shops. Any time you can safely preoccupy them for 15 minutes or so, take your chance.

When the kids know what's going on!

Small children are fairly easy to fob off, if indeed they notice that you've left the room at all. Older children, though, are quite a different matter.

You can still grab opportunities when they're away on sleepovers or out and about enjoying extracurricular activities. But waiting for them to go to bed is likely to become a thing of the past. For some parents, this is an anxious time for fear of being caught. One way to avoid this is to put a lock on the bedroom door. Some parents feel uncomfortable doing this, but if it happens early enough a child will learn to knock and accept it as the norm. If you've already got a lock on the bathroom door, you can also enjoy sex in the bath or shower.

It's important to put appropriate steps in place to maintain your sexual privacy. Not only does this reinforce your uniqueness as a couple, but it also sets a good example. There's nothing wrong with children knowing that adults have sex as part of loving relationships. A young child may not know what sex is, but they can understand that parents enjoy "special cuddles" or whatever euphemism you prefer to use. As children get older they will be more aware of sex and they will learn some valuable lessons from you. Adopting an attitude that says sex is natural, healthy, enjoyable, and private is an important message. One that they will hopefully remember when they're grown-ups.

Sex and aging

Sex in later life has many advantages. Most men will have lost their earlier physical urgency for satisfaction and many women feel more confident and comfortable with their sexuality. But this time of life is also a time when bodies are changing and many people begin to realize that they're not as fit as they used to be.

Fit for sex

The healthier and fitter you are, the better your sex life will be. As we age, our bodies become less supple and more prone to injury. Research has consistently shown that men and women who are fit and active enjoy more regular and more fulfilling sex lives.

As your body ages, your sexual needs and abilities also change. Maintaining an intimate relationship and a sexual environment will help you to talk about those changes together. Some of the physical changes will be due to the natural aging process, while others may be the result of illness or a side-effect of medication. Common illnesses such as heart disease, blood pressure problems, and diabetes directly affect sexual functioning, while other conditions such as arthritis have more of an indirect effect. But if you're both aware of those changes and ready and willing to accommodate them in your lovemaking, you can continue to enjoy an active and fulfilling sex life well into your eighties, or even nineties.

Changes in women

The changes in women's sexuality generally start with the menopause. For most women this begins from around age 50 and may last for between five and 15 years. The slow and gradual reduction of estrogen is responsible for the range of emotional and physical changes that women experience.

The most obvious physical symptoms are irregular and then absence of periods. Some women also suffer from hot sweats and flushes, drier hair and skin, and joint pain and tiredness. Emotional changes include feeling upset and irritable, difficulty concentrating, and changing sleep patterns. For many women, menopause is a difficult time, though most don't experience any severe problems. There is now a huge range of HRT (Hormone Replacement Therapy) choices available to help women manage the troublesome side effects. Check with your doctor for more information.

SHE SAYS ♀ ♂ HE SAYS

Since the menopause, things just seem to take longer than they used to. Longer to get aroused and longer to reach orgasm.

In general, I would say my sex life is better than ever. We have more time on our hands than we used to and sex can take as long as I need or want it too.

My sex life is definitely better now than it was 20 years ago. As a young man I struggled with premature ejaculation, which really knocked my confidence. Now, with a lot more skills in my toolkit, I know I can please a woman and enjoy making love to her as long as I like.

Changes in men

The reality of the male menopause, or andropause, is still being debated by the medical profession. There are conflicting views as to whether this is a physical or psychological condition in men. But most people do agree that a lot of men go through a "mid-life crisis."

Testosterone levels drop gradually over the male life cycle. It's thought that the symptoms experienced by many men during mid-life are caused by this drop. Those symptoms include tiredness and fatigue, increased irritability, reduced muscle mass, generalized aches and pains, sweating, and general low mood.

Most men also experience changes in their sexual functioning including lower sexual desire, taking longer to become aroused, and being slower to ejaculate. For some these are a problem, while for many men they see these side effects of aging as positively beneficial. Another common complaint is less firm erections, but they are usually still firm enough for penetration and most men quickly accept this as the norm.

Older men often make better, more confident lovers. With the urgency for orgasm reduced, most men are able to enjoy the intricacies of touch and pleasing their partner rather than worrying about their performance.

It's never too late to enjoy sex

Our media rarely portrays positive images of older couples enjoying sex, or even being naked. With images of virile, athletic young men making love to slim, nubile young women, it's really not surprising that many people assume that sex is only for the young and the beautiful.

But don't you believe it. Your genitals do not wither up and die decades before you do. As we've seen, sex does change as you become older, but it does not have to become any less enjoyable. Provided there's no debilitating illness, there is no reason why couples can't thoroughly enjoy sex as long as they live – in fact, they're likely to live longer if they do!

Contraception

There is an ever-growing choice of
contraceptive methods available, so
depending on how old this book is when
you read it, the following list may not be
up-to-date. Before you make any decision
about what method is best for you, be
sure to discuss it with your partner as
well as your doctor.

Barrier methods

These include the male and female
condom and the diaphragm. They're
readily available, have no side effects,
and provide additional protection against
sexually transmitted infections. However,
they can be fiddly to use and the
recommended accompanying
contraceptive creams can be messy.

Hormone options

These are the fastest-growing range of
options currently available. The
contraceptive pill is taken daily, and
the contraceptive injection, implant, or
patch, provides protection over a longer
period of time. The disadvantage of the
hormone options is that they're not
suitable for some women and they may
cause troublesome side effects.

Intra-uterine devices

There is now a range of devices that are
fitted by a health professional into the
uterus. The key advantage is that they
work for up to five years, but they can
sometimes cause heavier or more painful
periods. They're also not suitable for
all women.

Natural methods

By measuring body temperature, cervical
secretions, and/or hormone levels, a
couple can agree to abstain from
intercourse during the high-risk ovulation
period. The system is popular for those
who don't like medical intervention, but it
relies on stringent monitoring, good
organization, and a lot of will-power.

Permanent methods

If you're absolutely sure you *never* want
to have children then sterilization is an
option. Male sterilization (vasectomy) is
a more straightforward procedure than
female sterilization and has a quicker
recovery rate. Ask your doctor for
more information.

Sexual health

There are currently 25 different sexually transmitted infections. Some infections are very obvious and can be quickly and easily cured, while others are much harder to spot and can have devastating results if not treated. Symptoms vary from infection to infection and many STIs show no symptoms at all. Also, it's not uncommon to have more than one infection at the same time. Most STIs, if discovered soon enough, can be treated and cleared with a simple course of antibiotics. If you have any concern at all that you may have contracted something before you met your partner, or have put yourself at risk of catching something, then make an appointment to see your doctor as soon as possible.

Cystitis

Strictly speaking, cystitis is not a sexual infection, but extended lovemaking will make the condition worse and can kick off an inflammation – hence the expression "honeymoon cystitis." It is a very common condition and some women seem to be particularly prone to it. The bladder becomes inflamed due to a bacterial infection and the sufferer frequently needs to go to the bathroom and may experience pain when they go. The best treatment is to drink, drink, and drink some more. Preferably something alkaline that will neutralise the urine – cranberry or barley juice are favorites. Some sufferers also find it helpful if they go to the bathroom 10 to 15 minutes after sex and then drink lots. If the condition continues your doctor can prescribe antibiotics.

Thrush

This is a very common fungal infection that commonly affects the vagina and vulval area. It's very itchy and sex can be extremely uncomfortable and make the condition worse. Men may also catch the infection, but since they're less likely to have any symptoms he may inadvertently re-infect his partner. Like cystitis, it tends to be a condition that regularly reoccurs. There are a range of creams and pessaries available over the counter that quickly clear up the condition. Some women find going on a yeast-free diet stops the condition from reoccurring.

Index

Picture credits

Getty Images: pages 2, 5, 6–7, 8–9, 14, 19, 23, 28–29, 31, 37, 40, 43, 47, 49, 57, 58, 60–61, 63, 70, 72, 78–79, 81, 84–85, 87, 89, 96–97, 98, 100, 112–113, 119, 120–121, 123, 126–127, 130, 135, 138–139

Zefa: pages 27, 34, 44–45

Emma Farrarons: pages 92–93

Ann Summers: page 115
www.annsummers.com

Resources

The following professional organizations can direct you to certified sexuality couselors and provide information:

American Association for Marriage & Family Therapy (AAMFT)
www.therapistlocator.net

American Association of Sexuality Educators, Counselors & Therapists (AASECT)
Tel: 804 644 3288
www.aasect.org

Sexuality Information and Education Council of the United States (SIECUS)
Tel: 212 819 7990
www.siecus.org

For a good video series on sexuality:

Better Sex Video Series
The Sinclair Intimacy Institute
PO Box 8865
Chapel Hill
North Carolina 27515 USA
Tel: 800 955 0888
www.bettersex.com